Real-Life Math

Probability

by
Eric T. Olson

illustrated by Lois Leonard Stock

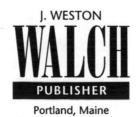
J. WESTON
WALCH
PUBLISHER
Portland, Maine

User's Guide
to
Walch Reproducible Books

As part of our general effort to provide educational materials that are as practical and economical as possible, we have designated this publication a "reproducible book." The designation means that the purchase of the book includes purchase of the right to limited reproduction of all pages on which this symbol appears:

Here is the basic Walch policy: We grant to individual purchasers of this book the right to make sufficient copies of reproducible pages for use by all students of a single teacher. This permission is limited to a single teacher and does not apply to entire schools or school systems, so institutions purchasing the book should pass the permission on to a single teacher. Copying of the book or its parts for resale is prohibited.

Any questions regarding this policy or request to purchase further reproduction rights should be addressed to:

Permissions Editor
J. Weston Walch, Publisher
321 Valley Street • P.O. Box 658
Portland, Maine 04104-0658

1   2   3   4   5   6   7   8   9   10
ISBN 0-8251-3811-6
Copyright © 1998
J. Weston Walch, Publisher
P. O. Box 658 • Portland, Maine 04104-0658
Printed in the United States of America

Contents

Foreword

You've seen it happen many times—a player in a dice game claims she is "due" for doubles; strangers discover that they have a mutual acquaintance and think that this must be more than a chance meeting; a friend plays the lottery obsessively or mails in sweepstakes entries with a persistent dream of winning. All these behaviors reflect how people perceive probability in daily life. People who lack an accurate sense of probability are easily drawn in by false claims and by pseudo-science, are vulnerable to get-rich-quick schemes, and exhibit many of the behaviors mentioned above.

The modeling and measurement of probabilities are fundamentals of mathematics that can be applied to the world around us. Every event, every measurement, every game, every accident, and even the nature of matter itself is understood through probabilistic models, yet few people have a good grasp of the nature of probability. Even students who have taken typical mathematics courses are unlikely to acquire the mathematical skills necessary to apply probabilistic models to real-world situations.

This book will help fill the gaps. This collection of activities will suppplement general math, pre-algebra, or algebra courses, and will add focus to a course dedicated to probability. The activities will help students develop the mathematical foundation needed to understand how probability works. There are two different sets of activities: One set (Activities 1–9) focuses on certain kinds of mathematical principles or processes that are needed to understand applied examples. The other set (Activities 10–26) provides some real-world examples of probabilistic models. The first set is important because students will be lost when they see a problem if they do not understand a few basic principles and do not have the ability to do basic calculations. The second set forms the bulk of the book, moving from simple experiments to more challenging applications.

After mastering the activities in this book, students will have tools to help them evaluate the probabilities of events they will encounter, and in the process they will learn to make better decisions in life.

Eric T. Olson
March 1998

1. Probability All Around Us

Context

Daily life

Math Topic

Random events

Overview

Probabilistic events affect everyday life in innumerable ways. In this activity, students are asked to make observations about events that have a random component.

Objectives

Students will be able to:

- describe a random event.

- state random and nonrandom properties of events.

Materials

- One copy of the Activity 1 handout for each student

Teaching Notes

To get students thinking about probability, ask them to come up with a list of events, games, and other everyday occurrences that have a perceived random property.

Discuss the concept of random events. If students are asked to name events in which the results are random, they should be able to come up with coin flips, dice rolls, playing card deals, lottery draws, and so on. These kinds of common events are certainly one type of phenomenon that can be considered, but many other phenomena have random components. In fact, nearly any observation of daily activities reveals some underlying randomness.

Emphasize that the outcome of a single random event or experiment of chance cannot be exactly predicted. The variability of a single event makes exact prediction of the outcome impossible. There is no way to know if a coin flip will yield heads or tails or if the weather will be rainy on a particular day six months from now. However, for a *large set* of repeated random events, there *is* a useful regularity. This regularity can be expressed by *probability*. Probabilities express the mathematical likelihood of each possible outcome of a random event. It must be strongly emphasized that probabilities may be measured only for large sets of repetitions. Using a corresponding probability model, mathematics may be used to make useful decisions about events having a random component.

Answers

1. The entries in the table on page 2 are meant to be concise. You might expound on the individual items in a class discussion. Answers will vary, but may include those given on the next page.

(continued)

1. **Probability All Around Us** *(continued)*

Event	Nonrandom Property	Random Property
Weather	Seasonal Change, local climate	Precipitation, temperature on specific days
Car accidents	Safe or unsafe driving practices	Specific cars or conditions met on the road
Class grades	Amount of study and preparation	Appearance of specific questions on tests
Customers at mall	Hours open, time of day	Specific pattern of customer arrival
State lottery	Decisions about games offered, prizes	Numbers drawn or winning patterns on tickets

2. The term "random" describes events that have underlying variability. Single random events cannot be predicted absolutely. However, using probability and probability models, it is possible to predict the total outcome of a large set of random events.

Extension Activity

Have students spend a day or more observing events with random properties and report back to class.

Name_____ Date _____

1. Probability All Around Us

After your third softball game in a row is rained out, you are talking with your teammates. One of them says, "Some things just seem to happen. We scheduled these games months ago, but who could have predicted so much rain?"

You ask, "I wonder if this is what our math teacher means by 'random events'?"

After your friends nearly tackle you for bringing up math at a time like this, you all start thinking about how many situations in daily life seem to happen randomly.

1. The table below lists five common events that have both random and nonrandom aspects. Explain what is random and what is not random about each. Then come up with five examples of your own.

Event	Nonrandom Property	Random Property
1. Weather		
2. Car accidents		
3. Class grades		
4. Customers at mall		
5. State lottery		
6.		
7.		
8.		
9.		
10.		

2. Describe what is meant by *random event*. Explain the relationship between probability and randomness.

_____

_____

_____

2. Counting Choices

Context

Choices in daily life

Math Topic

Multiplication

Overview

The most important mathematical concept for understanding probability is counting. More specifically, it is necessary to learn exactly *what* to count, along with the patterns involved in counting sometimes large numbers of possibilities. This activity is about counting through multiplication. The concept of probability is introduced for a set of equally likely outcomes.

Objectives

Students will be able to:

- count possible outcomes of random events.

- assign probabilities of equally likely events.

Materials

- One copy of the Activity 2 handout for each student

Teaching Notes

Students will discover how multiple choices of several different items can be multiplied to obtain the total number of choices. Explain to students that most of the work in determining the mathematical probability of an event is in counting the possible outcomes. The whole set of possible outcomes is called the *sample space*.

Answers

1. (a) $12 \times 8 \times 5 \times 2 = 960$;
   (b) 1/9 matched, 8/9 mismatched;
   (c) To determine the number of outfits that won't match, multiply the two non-matching sock pairs by half the shirt-and-pants combinations = $2 \times (12 \times 8) / 2 = 96$, so 96 out of 960 possible outfits will include socks that don't go with the outfit. On 1 out of 10 days, you will wear socks of the wrong color.
   (d) Answers will vary.

2. (a) There are $5 \times 3 \times 4$ or 60 possible meals.

   (b) There are $3 \times 1 \times 3$ or nine meals that you like. Your chance (probability) of getting a meal you like is only 9/60 or 15 percent.

2. Counting Choices

Our days are filled with choices. Sometimes it's confusing to even think about them.

1. In the morning you are always in a hurry, so you randomly choose clothes to wear from your closet (T-shirt, pants, socks, and shoes). You hope that what you pick out is not mismatched.

   (a) If you have 12 T-shirts, 8 pairs of pants, 5 different-colored pairs of socks, and 2 pairs of sneakers, how many different outfits are possible? (Luckily, your socks and shoes are always in pairs.)

   _____

   (b) If your socks all became separated, how often would you randomly pick out matched socks? mismatched socks?

   _____

   (c) If 3 out of 5 of your (matched) pairs of socks go with all of your shirt-and-pants combinations, and the other 2 pairs of socks go with half of your shirt-and-pants combinations, how often would you choose socks that don't match the rest of your outfit?

   _____

   (d) How could you buy clothes so that you would have the largest number of outfits for the least amount of money?

   _____

   _____

2. When you go to a local restaurant, there are 5 choices of sandwiches, 3 choices of potatoes, and 4 choices of soft drinks on the menu.

   (a) How many different meals are possible at this restaurant?

   _____

   (b) You like only 3 of the 5 sandwiches and 1 of the 4 kinds of soft drinks, but all 3 kinds of potatoes. If your friend brings you a meal selected at random from the restaurant's menu, what is the chance (the probability) that you will like it?

   _____

5   *Real-Life Math: Probability*

3. Independent Events and the Multiplication Rule

Context

Probability basics

Math Topic

Independence

Overview

Most of the examples in this book involve events that are independent. This means that one outcome or result is not influenced by another. Two events are independent if the result of the first event has no effect on the result of the second. Two coin flips are clearly independent, but there are cases where independence is not so clear. If events are independent, then an important mathematical rule of probabilities applies—the multiplication rule.

Objectives

Students will be able to:

- identify events that are independent.

- apply the multiplication rule to determine the probability of a sequence of independent events.

Materials

- Calculator

- One copy of the Activity 3 handout for each student

Teaching Notes

In the activity, students are asked to identify events that are independent and ones that are not independent. The criterion they should learn to look for is influence: Will one event influence the other? Ask students to propose other sets of events that are independent or not independent.

The remaining exercises are all applications of the multiplication rule for mathematical probabilities. Students should calculate the probability of the described sequence of events occurring. A few of the items do *not* involve independent events. In these cases, students should write "not independent" instead of calculating the probability.

Answers for Exercises

1. (a) independent;
   (b) independent;
   (c) not independent (removal of the aces increases the probability of drawing kings);
   (d) not independent (removing the first red ball increases the probability of drawing a white ball).

2. (a) NI;
   (b) $(1/6) \times (1/6) = 1/36$;
   (c) $(1/13) \times (1/13) = 1/169$;
   (d) $0.01 \times 0.01 = 0.0001$, or $1/10{,}000$.

Extension Activities

Have students come up with and study more events that are *not* independent. Three other activities involve such situations: Activity 8, Activity 19, and Activity 26.

Name_____ Date _____

3. Independent Events and the Multiplication Rule

Events are independent when one result is not influenced by another. Some events are clearly independent. Other cases are not so clear. The element to look for is influence. Will one event influence the other?

1. Decide whether or not the following sequences of events are independent. If they are, write "independent." If they are not, write "not independent" and explain why they are not.

   (a) Flipping a coin and getting heads, then flipping it again and getting tails

   _____

   (b) Rolling doubles with two dice, then rolling doubles again

   _____

   (c) Drawing (and removing) two aces from a normal deck of cards, then drawing two kings

   _____

   (d) Drawing (and removing) a red ball from a bag initially containing two red balls and three white balls, then drawing a white ball

   _____

2. Find the probability for each of the sets of events given below by using the multiplication rule if the events are independent. If they are not independent, write NI (for **Not Independent**).

   (a) Randomly choosing a person who is over 6 feet tall and weighs more than 250 pounds from a group of 100 people, among whom there are 13 people over 6 feet tall and 8 people who weigh more than 250 pounds

   _____

   (b) Rolling a 6 with one die, then rolling again and getting another 6

   _____

   (c) Drawing an ace from a normal deck of 52 cards, replacing the card, reshuffling, and drawing an ace again

   _____

   (d) Two separate machines, each 99 percent reliable (1 percent probability of breaking down), both breaking down

   _____

4. Factorials

Context

Probability basics

Math Topic

Discrete math

Overview

This activity focuses on a single mathematical operation: factorials. Many activities on probability use factorials, so it is critical that students recognize them and know how to work with them. Use this activity to be certain students have this knowledge before they do Activites 5 and 6.

Objectives

Students will be able to:

- recognize and compute factorials for nonnegative integers.

- realize that factorials become large quickly.

- evaluate simple mathematical expressions containing factorials.

Materials

- Calculator

- One copy of the Activity 4 handout for each student

Teaching Notes

Students may be baffled when they see the symbol "!" in a mathematical expression. Its meaning is simple: For an integer n, $n!$ means multiply all of the integers 1, 2, 3, . . . , n together to produce a result called "n fac-

torial." It's easy to calculate factorials up to about 11 with a simple calculator. Students should do this.

Have students evaluate expressions that contain factorials. The point here is to demonstrate that some expressions may be impossible to evaluate unless computations are performed in the correct order. The answers are actually simple to obtain. For example, 1001! / 1000! would be unwieldy if you attempted to compute 1000! and 1001! individually. However, if students realize that 1001! = 1000! × 1001, then 1001! / 1000! = (1000! × 1001) / 1000! = 1001. It is essential to understand this kind of operation, especially when working with combinations in the following activities.

Answers

1. (a) 1
   (b) 1
   (c) 2;
   (d) 6

   (e) 720
   (f) 362,880
   (g) 3,628,800
   (h) 39,916,800

2. (a) 6
   (b) 120
   (c) 100

   (d) 4950
   (e) 30,240
   (f) 35

Extension Activities

Have students use a simple 8-digit calculator and a scientific calculator to determine the largest factorial that will fit in the display window of each calculator. (8-digit calculator: 11! = 39,916,800; scientific calculator: 69! = 1.7112×10^{98})

4. Factorials

For an integer n, $n!$ means multiply all of the integers 1, 2, 3, ... , n together to produce a result called "n factorial" (Note: 0! is defined to equal 1). For example,

$$5! = 5 \times 4 \times 3 \times 2 \times 1$$

1. Calculate the following factorials:

(a) 0! = _____   (b) 1! = _____

(c) 2! = _____   (d) 3! = _____

(e) 6! = _____   (f) 9! = _____

(g) 10! = _____   (h) 11! = _____

2. Evaluate the following factorial expressions:

(a) 6! / 5! = _____   (b) 16! / (2! × 14!) = _____

(c) 100! / 99! = _____   (d) 100! / (2! × 98!) = _____

(e) 7! × 3! = _____   (f) 7! / (4! × 3!) = _____

5. Ways to Seat Guests: Permutations

Context

Entertainment

Math Topic

Discrete math

Overview

A permutation is an arrangement of a set of numbers, people, or objects in a row or other sequence. Once students understand how to take factorials, permutations are easy.

Objectives

Students will be able to:

- calculate the number of permutations of n distinct items.

Materials

- Calculator

- One copy of the Activity 5 handout for each student

Teaching Notes

The example of possible seating arrangements of guests around a table is used to help students understand the pattern involved when counting the number of possible arrangements of n distinct items into n identifiable positions. For the first position, any of the guests may be seated anywhere; hence there are n possibilities for this position. After the first guest has been seated, $(n - 1)$ possibilities are left for the second position, $(n - 2)$ for the third, $(n - 3)$ for the fourth, and so on. To get the total number of possibilities, multiply

$$n \times (n - 1) \times (n - 2) \times (n - 3) \times \ldots \times 1 = n!$$

So the total number of arrangements of n distinct items is $n!$

If there is a group of k (where k is greater than or equal to 2) identical or indistinguishable items in the set of n, then there are $k!$ equivalent arrangements for each permutation. Therefore, the total number of arrangements will be $n! / k!$.

Answers

1. (a) 5
   (b) 4
   (c) 3
   (d) 2
   (e) 1.

2. To find the total number of ways to fill all the seats, multiply the number of ways to fill each seat: $5 \times 4 \times 3 \times 2 \times 1$. This is the expression 5! or "5 factorial."

3. 5! = 120
   6! = 720.

5. Ways to Seat Guests: Permutations

Imagine that you have five dinner guests. While you are thinking about seating arrangements, you realize that there are many different ways you could seat your guests. But is there a way to figure out exactly how many arrangements are possible? Follow the instructions for question 1 exactly and in order. People are "available" until they are crossed out.

1. Pick a person to sit in seats A, B, C, D, and E one at a time and in order. Answer questions a–e one at a time as you fill in the name you have picked for each seat in the appropriate circle

   (a) How many people are available to sit in seat A? _____

   (b) How many people are available to sit in seat B? _____

   (c) How many people are available to sit in seat C? _____

   (d) How many people are available to sit in seat D? _____

   (e) How many people are available to sit in seat E? _____

2. In question 1 above, you counted the number of persons available to fill each seat. How could you figure out the total number of ways there are to fill all of the seats? Write this out as a mathematical expression. What is this mathematical expression called?

   _____

   _____

3. How many ways is it possible to arrange five people in five seats? six people in six seats?

   _____

     Real-Life Math: Probability

6. Ways to Choose Lunch Combinations

Context

Entertainment

Math Topic

Discrete math

Overview

Many problems in probability involve picking combinations of numbers or items from a much larger group. Several activities in this book require an understanding of combinations; students should have a firm grasp of combinations before they attempt these activities.

Objectives

Students will be able to:

- calculate the number of combinations of *n* things chosen *m* at a time.

Materials

- Calculator

- One copy of the Activity 6 handout for each student

Teaching Notes

Emphasize that factorials and permutations are essential for understanding combinations. The math used is similar. Students should have mastered the computations in Activity 4, Factorials, and Activity 5, Permutations, before going on to this activity.

Questions 1 and 2 of the activity allow students to develop a sense of combinations. They choose two food items from a group of six and write down the number of choices

they had. Multiplying the number of choices for each pick gives the total number of ways to pick.

The concept of order is introduced in question 3. The total number of possible selections must be divided by the number of ways to arrange each selection to obtain the number of unique selections.

Finally, students are given a fast, easy-to-remember method for finding any combination's result. You may wish to introduce the formal mathematical procedure:

$$\binom{n}{m} = \frac{n!}{m!(n-m)!}$$

Answers for Exercises

1. (a) 6
   (b) 5.

2. Multiply the number of possibilities for each choice: $6 \times 5 = 30$.

3. Since there are 2 equivalent arrangements of each choice, there are 30 / 2 or 15 unique choices. This represents enough combinations for a different lunch every weekday for 3 weeks. Be wary of students just multiplying 6×2 and not getting enough lunches.

4. (a) $4 \times 3 / 2! = 6$
   (b) $3 \times 2 / 2! = 3$
   (c) $20 \times 19 \times 18 \times 17 \times 16 \times 15 / 6! = 38,760$
   (d) $6 \times 5 \times 4 \times 3 \times 2 / 5! = 6$

6. Ways to Choose Lunch: Combinations

You invite a friend to join you at your favorite Mexican restaurant for the lunch special. You can choose any 2 different items for only 99 cents. There are 6 items to choose from. Your friend says, "I don't like to be bored. I would like to have a different combination every day, Monday through Friday, for at least 3 weeks, or I won't go with you." You say, "Relax, we can figure this out with math." Show how in this activity.

Soft Taco

Hard Taco

Enchilada ◯ A

Burrito ◯ B

Rice

Beans

1. (a) How many items are available to choose from for item A?
   _____ Pick any one of the items, cross it out, and write its name across circle A.

   (b) How many items are left to choose from for item B?
   _____ Pick any one of the available items, cross it out, and write its name across circle B.

2. How would you calculate the total number of ways to fill circles A and B? How many ways can you fill the circles?

   _____

3. You are not concerned about the order of A and B. In other words both taco-burrito and burrito-taco are considered as only one possible lunch. How many ways are there to choose lunch? Is this enough for 3 weeks of lunches so that your friend will stay happy?

   _____

4. There is an easy way to calculate the number of ways a certain number of items may be chosen from a larger group. First, determine the number of items you will choose. Then multiply the highest numbers together, until you have a number of factors equal to the number of items. For example, if you choose 3 objects from a group of 12, you would multiply $12 \times 11 \times 10$, the three highest numbers in the group. Then, if you are not concerned about the order of the objects chosen, divide by the number of ways you can arrange them. This is the number of permutations, equal to the factorial of the number chosen. In this case, the answer would be $(12 \times 11 \times 10) / 3!$ or 220 ways to select 3 objects from a group of 12. In mathematics, this is usually written $\binom{12}{3} = 220$. ($\binom{12}{3}$ can be read as "twelve choose 3.") If you are not concerned about order, how many ways are there to:

   (a) select 2 from a group of 4? _____   (b) select 2 from a group of 3? _____

   (c) select 6 from a group of 20? _____   (d) select 5 from a group of 6? _____

7. Password Possibilities

Context

Computers

Math Topic

Multiplication and exponents

Overview

Many kinds of electronic security depend on passwords. But there are a finite number of possibilities for passwords of finite length. This activity focuses on using multiplication and exponents to count possibilities.

Objectives

Students will be able to:

- count possible passwords using multiplication and exponents.

Materials

- Calculator

- One copy of the Activity 7 handout for each student

Teaching Notes

You may need to review the basics of exponents before proceeding. Students should know the meaning of mathematical statements like 2^{10} or 26^5. They will need their calculators and will need to know how to use them to find the values of expressions containing exponents.

The most interesting question is 1(d), which illustrates how many binary digits would be required in a code so that even the fastest computers could not guess every possible combination in a reasonable amount of time. You many want to convert answers in seconds to days or years.

Answers

1. (a) 2 or 2^1, Heads (H) or Tails (T)
   (b) 4 or 2^2, HH, HT, TH, and TT
   (c) 2^3, 2^4, 2^8, 2^{16}, and 2^{48}
   (d) Any answer 30 or lower is bad because the computer could check all the possibilities in 1 second or less. Even 40 coins would be inadequate because only 2^{10} or 1024 seconds would be required. Numbers larger than 100 would be adequate. The computer would require more than 1,013 years to check all the possibilities.

2. There are 12^3 or 1,728 possible combinations. The thief will test 50 percent in $(1728 \times 0.50)/100$ or 8.64 minutes.

3. (a) $26^3 = 17,576$
   (b) $26^5 = 11,881,376$
   (c) $26^6 = 308,915,776$

Extension Activities

- Students could research and report on the use of encryption in computer security.

- Ask students to speculate about why computer service providers recommend password that are at least eight characters long, and that us a combination of letters and numbers.

7. Password Possibilities

Combination locks are everywhere. You probably have one on a locker. But how secure is such a lock? And what about computer security? What is the probability that someone could hack into your computer or Internet account? It could happen unless you are careful about how you choose your password.

1. Let's say you want to build a security code based on coin tosses. Your code will be based on the outcome of one or more coins tossed at the same time. To break the code, an intruder (perhaps using a computer) must guess the exact pattern of heads and tails in your coin toss.

   (a) How many ways can a single tossed coin land? Write down the possibilities and write this number of possibilities as a power of 2.

   _____

   (b) How many ways can two tossed coins land? Write down the possibilities and write this number of possibilities as a power of 2.

   _____

   (c) How many possible ways can 3, 4, 8, 16, and 48 coins land? Write these numbers only as powers of 2.

   _____

   (d) A certain computer can check 2^{10} patterns of heads and tails per second. How many coins would be needed to make a code that is safe from this computer?

   _____

2. You have an old-style combination lock with three wheels, each containing 12 numbers. Exactly one combination of the three numbers must be selected to open the lock. A thief trying to open the lock checks 100 combinations per minute, at random. In how many minutes will there be a 50 percent probability that the thief will open the lock?

   _____

3. Computer services usually require passwords. Assume that you must choose a password using only the standard 26 letters (no symbols or numbers). How many different passwords can you choose with

   (a) 3 letters? _____

   (b) 5 letters? _____

   (c) 6 letters? _____

8. Setting Up a Basketball Tournament

Context

Sports

Math Topic

Combinations

Overview

When setting up a basketball tournament, organizers want the two best teams to have the highest probability of meeting in the final game. Past records are the only data available to help design the brackets.

Objectives

Students will be able to:

- study the number of possible combinations in an eight-team tournament.

- propose tournament pairings with the best chance of having the best teams in the final game.

Materials

- One copy of the Activity 8 handout for each student

Teaching Notes

The first question involves just figuring out how many ways an eight-team tournament could be set up. The result is surprisingly large. The second question asks students to eyeball the win–loss records and set up a tournament. Then they *guess* the probability that the final game would be a disappointment.

Answers

1. (a) 28   (d) 1
   (b) 15   (e) $28 \times 15 \times 6 \times 1 = 2,520$
   (c) 6

2. Student results will vary. The only requirement is that the Wolves and Bears meet in the final game.

3. This question requires students to guess the probabilities of the best teams not winning their first game, or winning the first then losing the second. These probabilities would be added to get the result. For example, say the Wolves are paired with the Sharks in the first game and the Wolves have a probability of only 0.05 of losing to the Sharks. They have a much higher probability of losing to any second-round opponent, say 0.25. Then the probability of the Wolves losing before the final game is $(0.05) + (0.95)(0.25) = 0.29$. Any reasoning along these lines is acceptable. There is a pretty good chance that one or both of the two best teams won't make the finals.

Extension Activities

Have students study pairings from recent sports tournaments and decide if the best teams did meet in the finals.

8. Setting Up a Basketball Tournament

You are the director of a basketball tournament. Eight teams are invited. You'd like to have the two best teams meet in the final game for the championship. Below is a table with the 20-game season records of all of the invited teams. (Some teams played teams not listed.)

	Wolves	Bears	Tigers	Lions	Eagles	Hawks	Bulldogs	Sharks
Won–Lost	19–1	18–2	15–5	12–8	8–12	7–13	6–14	3–17
Percent	0.95	0.90	.075	0.60	0.40	0.35	0.30	0.15

1. (a) How many different pairs of the eight teams are possible for games in the first round?

_____

(b) After one pair of teams is matched, how many different pairs from the remaining six teams are possible for the second game?

_____

(c) How many different pairs from the remaining four teams are possible for the third game?

_____

(d) How many pairs are left for the fourth game?

_____

(e) What is the total number of possible ways to set up pairs for the tournament?

_____

2. Set up the tournament using your best judgment about how to arrange pairings so that the two best teams will meet in the final game. Use the win–loss record above to guide you.

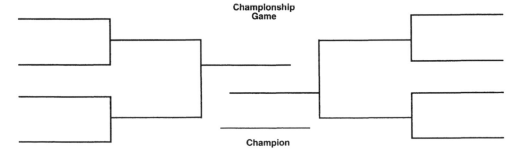

3. Guess the probability from your setup that the Wolves will be knocked out before the final round.

_____

9. Winning a Best-of-Seven-Game Series

Context

Sports

Math Topic

Combinations and multiplication rule

Overview

Mathematical *models* are often used to describe the pattern of data from an experiment. Most of the examples in this book follow simple models and have well-defined sample spaces. For example, tossing a coin has two possible outcomes, heads or tails. A series of such tosses can be shown to follow the *binomial model* studied in Activities 10–14.

However, in some situations the underlying probabilities can only be estimated from past experience. Sports is a good example. Two teams that meet in a best-of-seven-game playoff series often have played many times in the past. Given this experience, what is the probability that the underdog will win the series?

Objectives

Students will be able to:

- use combinations to find the number of ways a sports team can win four out of seven games in a playoff series.

- conduct simulations of playoff series to see how often the underdog wins.

Materials

- Calculator

- One random number table for each student (page 71 or 72)

- One copy of the Activity 9 handout for each student

Teaching Notes

These questions lead students through the process of using the binomial model for *independent* trials. This model allows calculation of the probability of m successes in n tries as long as the underlying probability is known. This probability may or may not be valid for sports teams in an actual playoff. But a long-term winning percentage of only 30 percent against an opponent makes the team discussed here a clear underdog. This could be a matter for class discussion.

Students are given hints about how to calculate outcomes and probabilities. They must apply what they have learned about combinations and the multiplication rule. You probably will need to help them. Here's a sample for a seven-game series in which the underdog wins only after game 7:

Number of ways team can win in seven
games = $\binom{6}{3} = \dfrac{6 \times 5 \times 4}{3 \times 2 \times 1} = 20$

Probability the underdog wins a seven–game
series = $\binom{6}{3}(0.3)^4(0.7)^3 = 20 \times 0.002778 = 0.05557$

(continued)

9. Winning a Best-of-Seven-Game Series *(continued)*

This activity is a good one to introduce the random number table. The simulation is very simple: Look up random numbers one at a time until one team wins four, then record the series winner and repeat. The underdog wins on 01 through 30. The opponent wins on 31 through 00 (00 represents 100). Make sure students use a new sequence of numbers for every series played.

Answers

1. (a) 1
   (b) 4
   (c) 20
   (d) $0.3 \times 0.3 \times 0.3 \times 0.3$ or 0.81%;
   (e) $4 \times 0.3 \times 0.3 \times 0.3 \times 0.3 \times 0.7$ or 2.3%;
   (f) $10 \times 0.3 \times 0.3 \times 0.3 \times 0.3 \times 0.7 \times 0.7$ or 4.0%;
   (g) $20 \times 0.3 \times 0.3 \times 0.3 \times 0.3 \times 0.7 \times 0.7 \times 0.7$ or 5.6%;
   (h) 0.81% + 2.3% + 4.0% + 5.6% or 12.7%.

2. Student results will vary. If there is enough time, a series-winning percentage of 13 percent will emerge with enough trials.

Extension Activity

Use sports record books for any sport with best-of-seven-game championship series to see how often the underdog wins.

9. Winning a Best-of-Seven-Game Series

You're a fan of a team that goes into a best-of-seven-game championship series with a dreaded opponent. But there's a big problem— your team has won only 30 percent, and has lost 70 percent, of its many games played against this opponent over the last couple of years. Your team is the clear underdog. Is there any hope? Yes, but they're going to need some luck . . . .

1. (a) How many outcomes are there in which your team wins a 4-game sweep? _____

   (b) How many outcomes are there in which your team wins with the 5th game? Remember, 3 of your team's 4 wins can come in any 3 of the first 4 games. _____

   (c) How many outcomes are there in which your team wins with the 7th game? Remember, 3 of your team's 4 wins can come in any 3 of the first 6 games. _____

   (d) What is the probability of your team sweeping 4 games? (Hint: Use the multiplication rule and their long-term winning percentage as the probability.) _____

   (e) What is the probability of your team winning in exactly 5 games? (Hint: Multiply the total number of outcomes where your team wins after 5 games by the probability of 4 wins and the probability of 1 loss) _____

   (f) What is the probability of your team winning in exactly 6 games? _____

   (g) What is the probability of your team winning in exactly 7 games? _____

   (h) What is the probability of your team winning the series? _____

2. A random number table gives you a way to test probability models. Your table has 1000 two-digit numbers selected completely at random. You can use it to simulate quickly many seven-game series to see how often your team wins.

   Pick numbers from the table one at a time in sequence. If any number from 01 to 30 comes up, your team wins a game. If 31 through 00 comes up, the opponent wins. As soon as one team wins a fourth game (this will happen in a maximum of seven games), the series is over. Record the winner below. Play as many series this way as you can. In what percentage of the series does your underdog team win?

Your team wins series:	Opponent wins series:
Total for your team:	Total for opponent:
Percentage of series won:	Percentage of series won:

10. Trials: Single Coin Toss

Context

Sports

Math Topic

Probability distributions

Overview

There is no better way to understand probability than to do simple experiments. Perhaps the easiest way to generate random events is to toss a coin.

Use Activity 11 if you wish to study the binomial model on which these trials are based.

Objectives

Students will be able to:

conduct and record the results of experimental trials.

make a graph to analyze the results.

Materials

- Calculator
- One copy of the Activity 10 handout for each pair of students
- One coin for each pair of students
- Graph paper

Teaching Notes

Students should pair off. Within each pair, one student will toss or spin the coin to produce good random trials. The other will record the results. Students should switch jobs halfway through the trials. It is recom-

mended that the person tossing the coin catch it rather than let it bounce on the floor.

Students will record 20 trials of 10 tosses each. The exact sequence of heads and tails in each trial should be written on the sheet. For each trial, the students should count and record the number of times the outcome was heads.

The students can then complete a histogram showing the frequency with which heads occurred 0 times, 1 time, 2 times, etc., up to 10 times in the trials.

If you decide to do Activity 11, make sure that students save their data from this activity.

Answers

1. and 2. Results will vary. The theoretical distribution of probability is

0H, 0.001	6H, 0.205
1H, 0.010	7H, 0.117
2H, 0.044	8H, 0.044
3H, 0.117	9H, 0.010
4H, 0.205	10H, 0.001
5H, 0.246	

For 20 iterations of the 10 flips, occurrences of 0H, 1H, 9H, and 10H will be rare, with total probability under 5 percent that any of these will happen. However, many students will experience one or perhaps two of these rare events within their 20 iterations. The rest of the theoretical distribution is 2H, 1 occurrence; 3H, 2 occurrences; 4H, 4 occurrences; 5H, 5 occurrences; 6H, 4 occurrences; 7H, 2 occurrences; 8H, 1 occurrence.

10. Trials: Single Coin Toss

You know there is a 50–50 chance that your team will win the coin toss at the beginning of a football game. But what is your team's probability of coming out ahead (or behind) in winning the toss during the course of a 10-game season? Find out in this simulation.

1. One partner will toss or spin a coin to produce good random trials. The other will record the results on this sheet. Switch jobs halfway through the trials. It is recommended that the person tossing the coin catch it rather than let it bounce on the floor. Record 20 trials of 10 tosses each. The exact sequence of heads and tails should be written on the sheet under "Outcomes." For each trial, record the number of times the outcome was heads out of the 10 tosses.

Trial	Outcomes	No. of Heads	Trial	Outcomes	No. of Heads
1			11		
2			12		
3			13		
4			14		
5			15		
6			16		
7			17		
8			18		
9			19		
10			20		

2. After all data are obtained, make a histogram on sheet of graph paper showing the frequency with which heads occurred 0 times, 1 time, 2 times, etc., up to 10 times in the trials.

11. Analysis: Single Coin Toss

Context

Simple experiment

Math Topic

Binomial model

Overview

In this activity, students use their data from Activity 10 to study the binomial model. Any independent trials built on events that have two possible outcomes, *success* or *failure*, fall under the binomial model. In this activity, students study the single coin toss, where success is defined as an outcome of heads and failure as an outcome of tails.

Objectives

Students will be able to:

- understand the binomial distribution.

- compare experiment and theory for 10 coin tosses.

Materials

- Calculator

- One copy of the Activity 11 handout for each student

- Data from Activity 10

Teaching Notes

To determine the likelihood of getting a certain number of heads out of 10 tosses of a coin, it is necessary to understand a mathematical model of this situation: the *binomial model*. This activity lets students calculate the binomial probabilities for their data and compare the calculated probabilities to their actual results.

The term *binomial* follows from the expression $(p + q)^n = 1$. When this expression is expanded into all of its binomial terms, the terms, each of which represents a certain number of successes and failures, all add up to 1. The general expression for an individual binomial probability (P) is

$$P_{n,m} = \binom{n}{m} p^m q^{(n-m)}$$

where n is the number of trials, m is the number of trials with successes, p is the probability of success, and q is the probability of failure $(1 - p)$.

It may be easier to teach students how to use the binomial model for a specific case. Say you want to know, before tossing a coin 10 times, the probability of getting 7 heads. First, you need to determine how many ways there are to "choose" 7 events (i.e., get heads 7 times) out of 10 events (i.e., 10 tosses), because *any* combination of 7 events being heads would result in a total of 7. From our discussion on combinations, we know there are $(10 \times 9 \times 8 \times 7 \times 6 \times 5 \times 4) / 7!$, or 120, such combinations.

Then, you must multiply this number by the probability of any individual series of 10 tosses coming out with 7 heads. The probability of heads (success) is ½, and the probability of tails (failure) is also ½. Because all 10 events are independent, this probability is $(½ \times ½ \times ½ \times ½ \times ½ \times ½ \times ½) \times (½ \times ½ \times ½) = (½)^7 \times (½)^3 = ½^{10} = 1/1024$.

The total probability of 7 out of 10 heads is $120 \times 1/1024 = 0.117$. Students should be able to calculate the remaining values.

(continued)

23

11. Analysis: Single Coin Toss *(continued)*

Answers

1. The distribution of total probability is

0H, 0.001	6H, 0.205
1H, 0.010	7H, 0.117
2H, 0.044	8H, 0.044
3H, 0.117	9H, 0.010
4H, 0.205	10H, 0.001
5H, 0.246	

See the answers for Activity 10 for additional comments.

2. Rarely will actual results exactly match the theoretical distribution. This would be a good point for a discussion about the nature of events with random properties and the meaning of mathematical probability. The most important lesson here is that the mathematical probability of ½ reflects a *distribution* of results with a mode at 5 of 10 tosses coming up heads.

Extension Activity

Have students recalculate the table assuming your trials involve *two* coins and that success is defined as an outcome of *both heads*. Run actual trials if desired. The probability of success is then ¼. Students will apply the binomial model for $p = ¼$ and $q = ¾$.

11. Analysis: Single Coin Toss

1. Complete the table showing the probability of each of the possible outcomes of a series of 10 coin tosses.

   Number of trials from Activity 10 _____

No. of heads	No. of combinations	Probability of individual outcome	Total probability	No. of heads from actual trials	Percent of heads from actual trials
0					
1					
2					
3					
4					
5					
6					
7					
8					
9					
10					

2. What have you learned about the meaning of a mathematical probability of ½ from observing and recording many actual events with this probability?

_____

_____

_____

12. Two Dice: When Will Doubles Occur?

Context

Games

Math Topic

Waiting times

Overview

Activity 12, Activity 13, and Activity 14 are designed to work together. You may do Activity 12 and Activity 14, Activity 13 and Activity 14, or all three activities.

Dice provide an excellent tool for studying the properties of independent events. When playing games involving dice or other random devices, many people feel that they become "due" for a particular outcome. In reality, for each repetition, the event has exactly the same probability.

Objectives

Students will be able to:

- understand that when independent events are repeated, outcomes do not depend on previous results.
- measure waiting times for discrete, independent events.

Materials

- Calculator
- One copy of the Activity 12 handout for each student
- Two standard six-sided dice for each student

Teaching Notes

First, students should create a chart showing all the possible outcomes for rolling a pair of dice. Each outcome has a probability of 1 of 36. Students should be able to conclude that six of 36 outcomes are doubles. Therefore, the probability of doubles is 6/36 = 1/6.

Next, each student should do his or her own trials. The results are easy to record because there is only one value to write down for each trial—the number of rolls that it took to get doubles. Sixty trials should take about 30 minutes.

Students are directed to wait for instructions after the trials. You may either proceed to Activity 13 to collect data concerning the *sum* on a pair of dice or go directly to Activity 14 to analyze the data.

Make sure students keep their data sheets for Activity 14. To get a larger sample size, combine everyone's data from this activity and then use Activity 14 as whole-class activity to analyze the data.

Answers

1. (a) 36
   (b) 6
   (c) 1/6
2. Student results will vary and will be analyzed in Activity 14.

Extension Activities

- Students may study games of chance that involve dice and report on the probabilities of various outcomes in the games.
- Students may expand their study to games with three or more dice.

12. Two Dice: When Will Doubles Occur?

You love to play Monopoly,® but you hate to land in jail. You need to roll doubles to get out. How long might you have to wait in jail? Do this activity to find out.

1. (a) How many total outcomes are in the sample space for two dice?

_____

   (b) How many outcomes are doubles?

_____

   (c) What is the probability of rolling doubles on a single roll?

_____

2. Conduct a series of trials in which you roll two dice repeatedly. Use the table below to record your results. A trial will consist of counting the number of rolls until doubles occurs. Record the number of rolls you count for each trial in the table. Start the next trial and count the number of rolls until doubles occurs again. If you don't get doubles after the twentieth roll, call the count 20 and start a new trial. Perform 30 to 60 trials, depending on the amount of available time.

Trial Number	Number of Rolls	Trial Number	Number of Rolls	Trial Number	Number of Rolls	Trial Number	Number of Rolls	Trial Number	Number of Rolls	Trial Number	Number of Rolls
1		11		21		31		41		51	
2		12		22		32		42		52	
3		13		23		33		43		53	
4		14		24		34		44		54	
5		15		25		35		45		55	
6		16		26		36		46		56	
7		17		27		37		47		57	
8		18		28		38		48		58	
9		19		29		39		49		59	
10		20		30		40		50		60	

Follow your teacher's instructions to report and analyze your data.

13. Two Dice: Sums

Context

Games

Math Topic

Waiting times

Overview

Activity 12, Activity 13, and Activity 14 are designed to work together. You may do Activity 12 and Activity 14, Activity 13 and Activity 14, or all three activities. These activities allow students to study the probabilities of the possible outcomes of rolling a pair of dice.

Objectives

Students will be able to:

- understand that when independent events are repeated, outcomes do not depend on previous results.

- measure waiting times for discrete, independent events.

Materials

- Calculator

- One copy of the Activity 13 handout for each student

- Two standard six-sided dice for each student

Teaching Notes

Students should first complete the chart showing the sums of all the possible outcomes for rolling a pair of dice. Each outcome has a probability of 1 in 36. Students should be able to add up the number of outcomes that represents each sum.

Next, each student should do his or her own trials. The results are easy to record because there is only one value to write down for each trial: the number of rolls it takes to get a chosen sum. Sixty trials should take about 30 minutes, but you may adjust the number of trials to accommodate the allotted time.

Students are directed to wait for instructions after the trials. You may either go to Activity 12 to collect more data concerning waiting for doubles or go directly to Activity 14 to analyze the data.

Make sure students keep their data sheets for Activity 14. To get a larger sample size, combine everyone's data from this activity and use Activity 14 as whole-class activity to analyze the data.

(continued)

13. Two Dice: Sums *(continued)*

Answers

1.

Possible Outcomes

Die 1

	1	2	3	4	5	6
1	2	3	4	5	6	7
2	3	4	5	6	7	8
3	4	5	6	7	8	9
4	5	6	7	8	9	10
5	6	7	8	9	10	11
6	7	8	9	10	11	12

Die 2 labels the rows.

Sum	Outcomes	Probability
2	1	1/36
3	2	1/18
4	3	1/12
5	4	1/9
6	5	5/36
7	6	1/6
8	5	5/36
9	4	1/9
10	3	1/12
11	2	1/18
12	1	1/36

2. Student results will vary and will be analyzed in Activity 14.

Extension Activities

- Students may study games of chance that involve dice and report on the probabilities of various outcomes in the games.

- Students may expand their study to games with three or more dice.

Name_____ Date _____

13. Two Dice: Sums

1. Complete the table below and at left showing the sums for all possible outcomes for rolling two dice. The first few possible outcomes are already recorded. Then record in the table below and at right the total number of outcomes and probability of rolling each possible sum:

Possible Outcomes

Die 1

	1	2	3	4	5	6
1	2	3				
2	3					
3						
4						
5						
6						

Die 2

Sum	Outcomes	Probability
2		
3		
4		
5		
6		
7		
8		
9		
10		
11		
12		

2. Pick a sum. Conduct a series of trials in which you roll two dice repeatedly. Use the table below to record your results. A trial will consist of counting the number of rolls until your sum occurs. Record the number of rolls for each trial in the table. Start the next trial and count the number of rolls until the sum occurs again. If you don't get your sum after the twentieth roll, call the count 20 and start a new trial. Perform 30 to 60 trials (according to your teacher's instructions).

Trial	Rolls	Trial	Rolls	Trial	Rolls	Trial	Rolls	Trial	Rolls	Trial	Rolls
1		11		21		31		41		51	
2		12		22		32		42		52	
3		13		23		33		43		53	
4		14		24		34		44		54	
5		15		25		35		45		55	
6		16		26		36		46		56	
7		17		27		37		47		57	
8		18		28		38		48		58	
9		19		29		39		49		59	
10		20		30		40		50		60	

Follow your teacher's instructions to report and analyze your data.

14. Analysis: Doubles or Sums

Context

Games

Math Topic

Waiting times

Overview

This activity is a continuation of Activity 12 and Activity 13. It provides an opportunity to analyze data from one or both of these activities and to take a deeper look at waiting-time distributions.

Objectives

Students will be able to:

• analyze data for waiting-time trials.

• Show graphically the frequency distribution of a waiting-time experiment.

Materials

• Calculator

• One copy of the Activity 14 handout for each student

• Graph paper

• Waiting-time data from Activity 12 or Activity 13

Teaching Notes

All students must have waiting-time data from Activity 12, Activity 13, or both. Students will work with calculators to tabulate and analyze their data. You may want to do this activity as a class exercise by combining everyone's data into one set of trials. If you do this, reproduce the summary table and distribution histogram on the board or the overhead projector.

Answers

1. (a) Students should enter *"DOUBLES"*, or *"SUMS"* along with the sum (2–12) that they were trying to achieve
   (b) for doubles, the theoretical probability is 1/6;
   for a sum:

of 2, 1/36	of 8, 5/36
of 3, 1/18	of 9, 1/9
of 4, 1/12	of 10, 1/12
of 5, 1/9	of 11, 1/18
of 6, 5/36	of 12, 1/36
of 7, 1/6	

2. (a) The table will reflect student results. This sample shows the theoretical values for a probability of 1/6 and 60 total repetitions. Trials seeking doubles or a sum of 7 have this probability. The table would look different for different probabilities. See Activity 9 for a discussion about how to find these values. Student results will rarely match exactly the theoretical results.

(continued)

14. Analysis: Doubles or Sums *(continued)*

Rolls	No. of Trials	% of Trials	Cuml. %
1	10	16.7%	16.7%
2	8	13.3%	30.9%
3	7	11.7%	41.7%
4	6	10.0%	51.8%
5	5	8.3%	60.0%
6	4	6.7%	66.7%
7	3	5.0%	71.7%
8	3	5.0%	76.7%
9	2	3.3%	80.0%
10	2	3.3%	83.3%
11	2	3.3%	86.6%
12	1	1.7%	88.3%
13	1	1.7%	90.0%
14	1	1.7%	91.7%
15	1	1.7%	93.4%
16	1	1.7%	95.1%
17	1	1.7%	96.8%
18	0	0.0%	96.8%
19	0	0.0%	96.8%
20*	2	3.3%	100.0%

* The frequency of 20 rolls is elevated because it
includes all values equal to or greater than 20.

(b) The cumulative percentage of doubles (or a sum of 7) occurring exceeds 50 percent by the fourth roll. In other words, in 50 percent of the trials, four or fewer rolls of the dice were necessary to achieve the desired outcome. Here are cumulative percentage values for the other sums: 2 or 12, more than 20 rolls; 3 or 11, thirteen rolls; 4 or 10, eight rolls; 5 or 9, six rolls; 6 or 8, five rolls.

3. Student results will vary. They will rarely match theoretical values, but in most cases, the histogram will show maximum values for one roll and steadily decreasing values for more rolls. For outcomes with lower probability, the histogram will be flatter.

Extension Activity

Have students set up computer spreadsheets to analyze waiting times.

14. Analysis: Doubles or Sums

1. This sheet is to be used to analyze your results from the waiting-times trials for doubles or sums. Please indicate whether this sheet is for doubles or sums trials. If it is for sums, indicate which sum you desired in your trials.

   (a) This sheet is for waiting-time trials for: _____

   (b) The theoretical probability for this outcome in a single trial is: _____

   (c) How many total trials were performed? _____

2. (a) In the table below, tabulate how many trials required the indicated number of rolls to reach the desired outcome. Calculate the percentage of trials for each number of rolls and the cumulative percentage of trials.

Rolls	No. of Trials	% of Trials	Cuml. %	Rolls	No. of Trials	% of Trials	Cuml. %
1				11			
2				12			
3				13			
4				14			
5				15			
6				16			
7				17			
8				18			
9				19			
10				20			

   (b) How many rolls are necessary before the probability of occurrence of the desired outcome is at least 50 percent?

   _____

3. Use a sheet of graph paper to make a histogram showing how often each number of rolls was required to get doubles or your selected sum from the data in your trials.

Applied Examples

Teacher
Guide
Page

15. Scrambled Word Puzzles

Context

Puzzles and games

Math Topic

Permutations and combinations

Overview

A common kind of word puzzle involves unscrambling several words with five or six letters and then using letters found in certain positions of the resulting words to decode a clever phrase. This activity gives students a chance to use their knowledge of permutations to solve puzzles of this kind.

Objectives

Students will be able to:

- recognize and apply knowledge of permutations to the solution of a scrambled word puzzle.

Materials

- One copy of the Activity 15 handout for each pair of students

Teaching Notes

This activity is meant to be fun; it should be used as a break from the normal routine. But there are also learning objectives that your students should have achieved and should be able to apply in this activity. Specifically, they should be able to answer the questions concerning the total number of possible permutations of any number of distinct letters. Some creative thought should allow them to figure out the permutations possible if letters are restricted to certain positions or if letters repeat.

Answers

1. There are four distinct letters, so there are 4! or 24 possible permutations: AGNT, AGTN, ATGN, ATNG, ANGT, ANTG, GANT, GATN, GNTA, **GNAT**, GTNA, GTAN, NAGT, NATG, NGAT, NGTA, NTAG, NTGA, TAGN, **TANG**, TGAN, TGNA, TNAG, TNGA. There are two actual words, *gnat* and *tang*.

2. (a) 5! or 120
   (b) 6! or 720
   (c) There are three identical letters, so for each permutation there are 3! or 6 equivalents. The total is thus 120/6 or 20 possible arrangements
   (d) There are 3! or 6 ways to arrange the letters in each group, so there are 6×6 = 36 ways to arrange these letters, significantly fewer than the 720 possible ways when all six letters are separate rather than in groups.

3. **HENCE, COUNT, EXPECT, RANDOM**; The probability of getting the television controller away from your friend: A **REMOTE CHANCE**. Students may use strategies, such as trying different permutations or trying to solve the puzzle first, to narrow down the number of possible arrangements of the letters.

Extension Activity

Have students search the Internet for sites concerning scrambled word puzzles. Some such sites have interactive programs that supply answers for scrambled words. Ask students to speculate on how such programs might work.

15. Scrambled Word Puzzles

Many daily newspapers carry a puzzle where four or five words are scrambled. You figure out what the words are, then use letters found in certain positions of these words to decode a joke or clever phrase. You can use your knowledge of probability to solve this kind of puzzle.

1. How many ways is it possible to arrange the following four letters: A, G, N, T? Write all of the possibilities below. How many of the possible arrangements are actual words?

_____

   Number of possible arrangements _____

   Number of actual words _____

2. How many ways is it possible to arrange

   (a) five distinct letters? _____   (b) six distinct letters? _____

   (c) the letters GEESE? _____   (d) two groups of three distinct letters? _____

3. Complete the puzzle below. Describe any strategies that you used to unscramble the words.

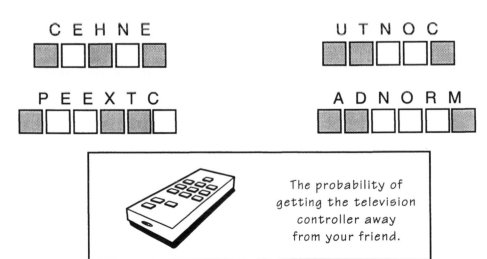

Probability Puzzler

Unscramble these four words, putting one letter in each square, to form four words related to probability.

C E H N E

U T N O C

P E E X T C

A D N O R M

The probability of getting the television controller away from your friend.

Now arrange the letters in the gray boxes to form the final answer. The cartoon above provides a clue.

A ▢▢▢▢▢   ▢▢▢▢▢

Real-Life Math: Probability

16. Number of Boys and Girls in a Family

Context

Families

Math Topics

Geometric distribution and averages

Overview

This topic is a further application of probability principles learned in Activities 9–14. Assuming that for a live birth, the probability of a baby of either sex is ½, the situation is similar to tossing a coin. In this activity, students will calculate the probabilities of various family compositions of boys and girls, then conduct trials concerning waiting times for a family to have at least one boy *and* one girl. The concept of an *average* (or *expected value*) is introduced.

Objectives

Students will be able to:

* calculate the probabilities of family composition for families of up to six children.

* determine the *average* of a set of trial data concerning family composition.

Materials

* Calculator

* One copy of the Activity 16 handout for each pair of students

* One coin or a random number table for each pair of students (see pages 71 and 72 for random number tables)

Teaching Notes

The assumption that the probability of a new baby being a girl (or a boy) is exactly ½ is fundamental to this activity. You may want to discuss this as a class, or as an extension, you might ask students to research actual statistics. There are many interesting possibilities here, especially if sex distribution is considered in countries other than the United States.

This probability is a *geometric distribution*. The distribution starts at two children (because there must be at least two to have a boy and a girl). So the probability (*P*) of *n* children (*n* > 1) is thus

$$P(n) = \left(\frac{1}{2}\right)^{(n-1)}$$

The activity considers parents who plan to stop having children when they have at least one boy and one girl. The trials may be conducted with a coin or a random number table.

After the trials are completed, students are asked to find the *average* number of children in a family with the given conditions. Make sure students know how to find an average (or *mean*). The average is equal to the sum of the counts from all trials divided by the number of trials.

(continued)

16. Number of Boys and Girls
in a Family *(continued)*

Answers

1. Student results for the table will vary.

2. Students could count the number of trials in which the number of kids is greater than 4, then divide by the total number of trials. Theoretically, 7/8 of the trials will yield 2, 3, or 4 children, and 1/8 will have higher values.

3. The theoretical average is 3 children.

Extension Activities

- Have students research factors that affect family size and composition.

- Have students develop the following probability table for family composition for families with one to six children using the binomial model. Note that the total probability for each line sums to 1.

Children in family	0 girls	1 girl	2 girls	3 girls	4 girls	5 girls	6 girls
1	1/2	1/2					
2	1/4	1/2	1/4				
3	1/8	3/8	3/8	1/8			
4	1/16	1/4	3/8	1/4	1/16		
5	1/32	5/32	5/16	5/16	5/32	1/32	
6	1/64	3/32	15/64	20/64	15/64	3/32	1/64

16. Number of Boys and Girls in a Family

A young couple is discussing how many children they want to have. The man says, "Let's have as many children as necessary until we have at least one girl and one boy, then stop."

The woman says, "I'll go as high as four. After that, you can bear the children yourself."

What is the probability that they can achieve their desired family size and composition?

1. To answer the above question, conduct trials with a random number table. A trial will consist of counting random numbers until there is at least one even number (representing a girl) and one odd number (representing a boy) in the series. Record your count until an even and an odd number are obtained for each trial in the table below. This count will represent the total number of kids in the family. The minimum count for each trial is 2. (Alternately, you may toss a coin to conduct the trials, counting the number of flips until you have one head and one tail.)

Trial	Kids	Trial	Kids	Trial	Kids	Trial	Kids	Trial	Kids	Trial	Kids
1		11		21		31		41		51	
2		12		22		32		42		52	
3		13		23		33		43		53	
4		14		24		34		44		54	
5		15		25		35		45		55	
6		16		26		36		46		56	
7		17		27		37		47		57	
8		18		28		38		48		58	
9		19		29		39		49		59	
10		20		30		40		50		60	

2. What is the probability that the result is four children or fewer? _____

3. What would be the *average* number of children for a large number of families where parents have children until they have at least one boy and one girl? _____

                                       Real-Life Math: Probabilty

17. Chance of a Hitting Streak

Context

Sports

Math Topic

Waiting time

Overview

In baseball and softball, individual performances are the key to team success. Players are rated by many statistics, the most important of which is the batting average. This statistic is really a probability: the number of times out of 1,000 that a player gets to base safely by hitting the ball, and no defensive player makes an error.

It's common for players to "streak," that is, to experience hot periods with many hits or cold periods with few hits. In this activity, students explore the probabilities of players' hitting streaks given their batting averages.

Objectives

Students will be able to:

• calculate the probabilities of a player with a particular batting average either getting a hit or not getting a hit in a game.

• determine the *average* hitting streak from a set of trial data.

Materials

• Calculator
• One copy of the Activity 17 handout for each pair of students
• One random number table for each pair of students (see pages 71 and 72 for random number tables)

Teaching Notes

This activity is similar to Activity 16 in that it considers waiting times. Students must calculate the probabilities of a player with a given batting average getting at least one hit out of four at-bats (consider four at-bats to be a "game") and getting no hits out of four at-bats. Then they run trials to determine the probability of having several games in a row with at least one hit (a "hitting streak").

To run the trials, students use the probability for getting a hit in a game that they have calculated in 1(c). They round this probability to 2 significant digits. Their success is achieved when a number from 01 through the two-digit value appears on the random number table. Students should be aware that probabilities add to 1, so $P(A) = 1 - P(\text{not } A)$.

Answers

1. It is easier to do part (b) first. The probability of no hits is $(1 - \text{batting average})^4$. So the answers are (a) probability of at least one hit = (1 – probability of no hits) = $1 - (1 - \text{batting average})^4 = 1 - (0.68)^4 = 0.786$; (b) $(1 - \text{batting average})^4 = 0.214$.

2. Answers will vary.

3. Student answers will vary with respect to the average chosen and the individual trials.

Extension Activities

• Use the newspaper to track hitting streaks of major league baseball players.

• Students may want to track the streaks of players on a school or other local team.

17. Chance of a Hitting Streak

Hitting streaks (consecutive games getting a hit) are one of the most exciting individual performance statistics in baseball and softball.

1. (a) If a baseball or softball player has a batting average of .320, what is the probability that he or she will get at least one hit in a game? Consider a game always to consist of four at-bats, and assume that at-bats are independent.

    _____

   (b) What is the probability that he or she will get no hits in a game?

    _____

2. Conduct 60 trials in which you try to achieve the longest hitting streak possible for a hitter whose batting average you choose. Use a random number table to conduct the trials. Round the probability of getting a hit to two digits. If a value greater than or equal to your calculated probability comes up, the streak ends. Write the number of games that the streak lasts in the table below.

Trial	Games	Trial	Games	Trial	Games	Trial	Games	Trial	Games	Trial	Games
1		11		21		31		41		51	
2		12		22		32		42		52	
3		13		23		33		43		53	
4		14		24		34		44		54	
5		15		25		35		45		55	
6		16		26		36		46		56	
7		17		27		37		47		57	
8		18		28		38		48		58	
9		19		29		39		49		59	
10		20		30		40		50		60	

3. (a) What was your batter's longest hitting streak? _____

   (b) What was your batter's average hitting streak (number of games)? _____

18. Two People in a Group With the Same Birthday

Context

Coincidences

Math Topic

Data collection and analysis

Overview

Unexpected coincidences often draw gasps. A famous problem in probability—calculation of the chance that at least two people in a small group share a birthday—illustrates that some kinds of coincidences are not at all unlikely.

Objectives

Students will be able to:

- determine through simulation the probability of at least two people in a group having a common birthday.

Materials

- Calculator

- For each class member, a set of two small paper bags, with one bag containing month names and the other containing dates obtained by cutting up copies of the Random Date Template from the Appendix.

- One copy of the Activity 18 handout for each pair of students

Teaching Notes

Allow students to guess how often at least two people in a random group of students in a class your size will have the same birthday. Some people tend to guess that this is a rare occurrence because 367 people are required for a group *guaranteed* to have at least two members sharing a birthday.

This simulation will require the Random Date Template found in the Appendix, prepared as described above. The instructions here assume that the simulation will be a whole-class project. The sets of month and date bags should be distributed to each member of the class.

For each trial, each student should shake up both bags, then draw out a single slip from each bag. If a student draws a date that does not exist for the drawn month, the student should draw another date without replacing the first slip. February 29 should be allowed, even though this birthday is less likely than any other. After the trial is recorded, all of the slips must be returned to the proper bags and the bags must be shaken up again. Just for fun, students may use their actual birthdays instead of drawn ones for one trial.

Students should report their drawn birthdays to a recorder at the board or at an overhead projector. If after all birthdays are reported, no two match, the trial should be recorded "fail." If *any* two students reported matching birthdays, the trial should be recorded "success."

Do as many trials as time allows. There are 30 spaces on the record sheet.

(continued)

18. Two People in a Group With the Same Birthday *(continued)*

Answers

1. (a) and (b) Student answers will vary. If students are reluctant to make a prediction, throw out some proposals. For example, say, "How many think 1 percent?"

2. Results will vary.

3. (a) Here are all of the theoretical probabilities of at least one pair of common birthdays for group sizes from 2 to 35 students:

2, 0.3%	19, 37.8%
3, 0.8%	20, 41.1%
4, 1.6%	21, 44.3%
5, 2.7%	22, 47.5%
6, 4.0%	23, 50.6%
7, 5.6%	24, 53.7%
8, 7.4%	25, 56.8%
9, 9.4%	26, 59.7%
10, 11.7%	27, 62.6%
11, 14.1%	28, 65.3%
12, 16.7%	29, 68.0%
13, 19.4%	30, 70.5%
14, 22.3%	31, 72.9%
15, 25.2%	32, 75.2%
16, 28.3%	33, 77.4%
17, 31.4%	34, 79.4%
18, 34.6%	35, 81.3%

Note that for a group of 23, the probability is about 50 percent. For 35, it is more than 80 percent.

(b) Johnny Carson's experiment failed because he asked the audience if anyone had a particular birthday. In this experiment, students test for any two people having the *same* birthday.

Extension Activity

Develop the mathematical model for the probabilities of common birthdays.

Name_____ Date _____

18. Two People in a Group With the Same Birthday

Some years ago on the *Tonight Show With Johnny Carson*, a guest explained that there is a high probability two people in a small group will have the same birthday. Johnny asked the audience of about 150 if anyone had *his* birthday. No one did. But the guest was not a mathematics student and couldn't find the flaw in Johnny's test. In this activity, you will perform an accurate test of the guest's statement.

1. (a) How many students will participate in your group? _____

(b) Make a prediction—in what percentage of trials do you *think* there will be at least one pair of common birthdays? _____

2. You have been given two small bags to use in your trial. One bag contains the names of the months of the year. The other contains dates. To perform trials, you will draw random birthdays as follows for each trial.

First, shake up the slips in your bags. Draw only one slip from each bag. One of the slips is your month, the other is your date. When it's your turn, report this birthday to the class. If you draw a date that doesn't exist for the month you draw—for example, September 31st—draw another date without replacing the first slip. Although a birthday of February 29th is less likely than any other, it should be allowed.

After all class members have reported birthdays, determine if any two of them match. If there are any matches, report the trial as "success." If there are no matches, report the trial as "failure." Check the appropriate box on the table on the next page.

(continued)

18. Two People in a Group With the Same Birthday (continued)

Trial	Success	Failure	Trial	Success	Failure	Trial	Success	Failure
1			11			21		
2			12			22		
3			13			23		
4			14			24		
5			15			25		
6			16			26		
7			17			27		
8			18			28		
9			19			29		
10			20			30		
						Total		

3. (a) What percentage of all trials were reported as "success" and what percentage were reported as "failure?" How does this compare with your original prediction?

_____

_____

(b) What was wrong with Johnny Carson's experiment? _____

_____

_____

19. Medical Testing

Context

Health

Math Topic

Conditional probability

Overview

This activity introduces a sometimes subtle process in probability—what happens to probability once some new or additional fact about a situation is known. This is called "conditional probability" and can be quite confusing. Here students study a real-life problem concerning medical testing. No simulation is included here. (In Activity 30, another counterintuitive example of conditional probability concerning the three-door problem is examined. Activity 30 includes a simulation.)

Objectives

Students will be able to:

- demonstrate that in medical testing, even a seemingly high accuracy rate can lead to a high rate of false positives.

Materials

- Calculator
- One copy of the Activity 19 handout for each student

Teaching Notes

This activity is designed to get students thinking about conditional probability—if *A* happens, what is the probability of *B* given *A?*

You may want to try a couple simple examples with the class.

- Tell students you have rolled a pair of dice which add up to *at least* 11. Ask them what the probability is that you have, in fact, rolled a 12. The answer is 1/3. Once it is known the sum is at least 11, there are only three outcomes possible—5 & 6, 6 & 5, or 6 & 6, all equally likely. One of the three has a sum of 12.

- What is the probability that a card drawn is a face card? The answer is 12/52 or 3/13. What is the probability that a card drawn is a jack if you already know it is a face card? The answer is 1/3, because a jack is one of three possible face cards. How about the probability that a card is a face card if you already know it is a jack? The answer is 1, because all jacks are face cards.

It is very easy to jump to conclusions when an impressive number, for example a high accuracy rate, is given. Medical testing is a prime example. Many conditions are relatively rare. In question 3, the rate of occurrence is only 0.2 percent (200 out of 100,000). If a test on an individual is 99 percent accurate, the number of possible false positives on a condition with a 0.2 percent occurrence rate leads to a shocking rate of false positives. The important lesson here is to ask questions and understand probability when dealing with medical tests!

(continued)

19. Medical Testing *(continued)*

If the students should ask, of the 99,800 who do *not* have the condition, 98,802 will test negative. Of the 200 who *do* have the condition, 2 will test negative (false negatives). Only 2 of 98,804 or 0.002 percent will be false negative tests.

Answers

1. (a) 100,000 – 200 or 99,800 do not have the condition
   (b) 200
   (c) 0.99×200 or 198 of the 200 people who *do* have the condition will test positive, since the test is 99 percent accurate
   (d) $0.01 \times 99,800$ or 998 will falsely test positive since the test is 99 percent accurate
   (e) 198 + 998 = 1196 tests will be positive; (f) 198 / 1196 = 0.166 or 16.6 percent of positive tests are true positives
   (g) 998 / 1196 = 0.834 or 83.4 percent of positive tests are false positives!

2. The result in this example that only 16.6 percent of positive tests are true positives is very surprising. An impressive-sounding 99 percent accuracy rate can mean little if the test is for a relatively rare condition. Many medical tests are more useful for ruling *out* a condition, not proving that it exists. When you are dealing with medical tests, always ask your medical professional for rates of false positives! If a test comes back positive, always ask for confirmation from alternate tests or ask for another opinion.

Extension Activities

- Ask students to investigate Bayes' Theorem. The calculations in these exercises all follow from this result first proved by Thomas Bayes in the eighteenth century.

- Have students answer the questions on the handout again, this time assuming that the test is given twice to each person and that two positives are required to test positive.

Name_____ Date _____

19. Medical Testing

Should you be concerned about the accuracy of tests for medical conditions? For example let's say a test for a medical condition is 99 percent accurate when it is given to one individual. Impressive, right? This means that on average, if 100 people are tested, 99 of the tests will give a correct result (negative or positive), and 1 will show an incorrect result. However, over a long time period, let's say that experience has shown that 200 out of 100,000 people in the entire population actually have this condition.

1. (a) If 100,000 people are tested, how many of those 100,000 do *not* actually have the condition?

_____

(b) How many of the 100,000 people actually *do* have the condition?

_____

(c) Of the number of people who actually *do* have the condition, how many will test positive? Explain your answer.

_____

(d) Of the number of people who do *not* have the condition, how many will *falsely* be shown by the test to be positive for the condition?

_____

(e) What is the total number of positive tests out of the 100,000 tests administered?

_____

(f) Given that a test is positive, what is the conditional probability that the person tested actually has the condition?

_____

(g) Given that a test is positive, what is the conditional probability that the person tested does *not* have the condition (the test falsely shows a positive result)?

2. Comment on the results of these calculations of conditional probability. What questions should you ask a medical professional when you are tested for a medical condition?

_____

_____

20. Lotto Games: Winning the Big One?

Context

Recreation

Math Topic

Combinations

Overview

Participation in state-run lotteries has become a common recreational activity for millions of people. But how likely is a big lotto win? This activity gives students a chance to apply their knowledge of combinations and probability to develop a sense of reality about this question.

Objectives

Students will be able to:

- calculate lottery odds using combinations.

- demonstrate a sense of the chance that an individual will win a lottery.

Materials

- Calculator

- One copy of the Activity 20 handout for each student

- One copy of the Mock Lotto Tickets sheet (see Appendix) for each pair or small group of students

Teaching Notes

This activity is based on the Florida state lottery. However, many other state lotteries operate similar games, and this activity could be modified to work with any of them.

Run the activity by following these steps:

- Prior to class, find the most recent winning number from Florida Lotto (or another lottery of your choice). This can easily be found on the Internet at http://www.flalottery.com.

- Students are first asked to analyze individually the total number of combinations of six distinct numbers that can be formed by choosing integers from 1 to 49. They will apply their knowledge from Activity 6 to perform this calculation. Students should calculate the total number of possible combinations and understand that the probability of a single ticket winning the big prize is 1/(total number of possible combinations).

- Next, have the students organize into pairs or small groups. Distribute the Mock Lotto Tickets sheet to each group This sheet contains 120 randomly generated combinations of six numbers picked from the integers 1 through 49.

- Announce the winning number from the most recent Florida Lotto. The students should check the winning combination of numbers against all of the combinations on the Mock Lotto Tickets. They should report how many mock combinations match 0, 1, 2, 3, 4, 5, or 6 of the numbers in the winning combination using the bar chart provided.

(continued)

20. Lotto Games: Winning the Big One? *(continued)*

- Students will find that they will rarely record a ticket with more than three matching numbers. The last question gives them the opportunity to comment on the reality of winning lottery games.

Answers

1. The total number of combinations is
   49! / 43!(6!) = $(49 \times 48 \times 47 \times 46 \times 45 \times 44) / (6 \times 5 \times 4 \times 3 \times 2 \times 1)$ = 13,983,816.
   The probability of winning on a single ticket is 1/13,983,816 or 0.0000000715.
   (Note that, on average, if you play one ticket every day, it would take 38,312 years to win!)

2. Theory suggests that of the 120 mock tickets, 52 will match none of the numbers from the winning combination, 50 will match 1 of the numbers, 16 will match 2, and 2 will match 3. Note that that's a total of 120. Tickets for which there will be more than three matching numbers will be rare. Furthermore, actual results will almost never match the theoretical values.

3. Because even three matched numbers is unusual, students may fairly respond that nearly everyone loses their money by playing the lottery.

Extension Activities

- This activity might be extended over several weeks and multiple drawings.

- Some students might be able to write computer programs to generate and test mock tickets.

20. Lotto Games: Winning the Big One?

1. How many possible combinations of 6 distinct integers may
   be chosen from the integers 1 through 49?

_____

This is the total number of possible combinations of numbers that may be chosen in
Florida Lotto. Many other state lotteries have similar numbers of possibilities. What is
the probability of a single ticket winning the Florida Lotto?

_____

2. Write the most recent winning number combination from the Florida Lotto here:

_____

Work with a partner or a small group. Check each combination of 6 numbers from the
Mock Lotto Tickets sheet and record the number of tickets having 1, 2, 3, 4, 5, or 6 numbers
that match numbers in the winning combination. Make a bar chart to tabulate the results:

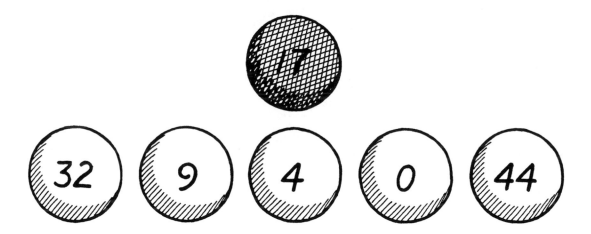

3. Your ticket must match three numbers to win a prize. What is the usual outcome of
   playing a state lotto game?

_____

21. Waiting for the Academy Award®

Context

Recreation

Math Topic

Waiting time

Overview

Few actors get a chance to act in big-name movies. But after an actor does make it big, what is the probability that the actor will win an Academy Award (Oscar®) in any given year, or over an entire career? Some famous actors have waited decades and have worked in dozens of movies before winning an Oscar, while others have won for their very first movie. In truth, the probability of an actor winning one of the top awards for movie acting in any year is small.

Objectives

Students will be able to:

- estimate probabilities through rough assumptions.

- simulate an individual actor's chance of winning an Oscar.

Materials

- One copy of the Activity 21 handout for each student

- One random number table for each pair of students (see Appendix)

Teaching Notes

All assumptions about probability in this activity are extremely rough. The estimate of 200 available actors is based on the list of entertainment personalities and notable movies in the *World Almanac and Book of Facts 1998*. Students could investigate this for themselves.

There is no real reason to think that all movie actors will have an equal probability of winning each year. Many will be up in popularity, others down. Some will be more active, others less so. And the kinds of movies produced change every year, making some actors more desirable. However, the assumption of equal probabilities provides the easiest method for analyzing this simple model.

The simulation in part 2 shows that for even a very talented actor to win an Oscar, many things must fall into place. Good luck has much to do with it. Students are asked to design an experiment in which they pretend to be actors themselves. Give half of the students Random Number Table 1, the other half Random Number Table 2 (these tables are in the Appendix). Ask the students to start at different positions in the tables.

A trial would go like this—the first probability (getting a good role) is ½; say that a random number between 50 and 99 would mean success and 00 to 49 would mean failure. The second and third probabilities (getting a nomination and getting the award) are each ⅕, so for second and third random numbers, numbers between 80 and 99 would mean success and between 00 to 79 would mean failure. To win an award in any year, all three must be successes.

(continued)

21. Waiting for the Academy
Award® *(continued)*

Students should keep careful count of the three random numbers for each year and should record the years (if any) in which they win. Just for fun, let the students make up names of movies and short descriptions of the roles for which they win or are nominated.

Answers

1. 1/50, assuming that the pool of actors is half male and half female.

2. (a) Student results will vary. There is a $1 - (0.98)^{50}$ or 64 percent probability that an actor will win the award before the fifty-first year.

   (b) See the Teaching Notes.

Extension Activity

Students could investigate past Academy Award winners and the number of years into their careers that they received awards. From this research, they could study factors that improve an actor's probability of receiving an Oscar.

21. Waiting for the Academy Award®

The crowning achievement for an actor's career is winning an Academy Award (an Oscar®). There are four acting awards each year—Best Actor, Best Actress, Best Supporting Actress, and Best Supporting Actor. But how many actors ever achieve this honor?

Some actors had decades of great performances before winning. Henry Fonda finally won Best Actor for *On Golden Pond* in 1982 after a 50-year career. Jessica Tandy was recognized after a stellar 60-year career with a Best Actress Oscar for *Driving Miss Daisy* in 1989. And Martin Landau waited 40 years and acted in more than 20 films before winning Best Supporting Actor for *Ed Wood* in 1994.

On the other hand, some actors have won very early in their careers. For example, Marisa Tomei won Best Supporting Actress in her first big film, *My Cousin Vinny*, in 1992. Cuba Gooding, Jr., won for his first major film, *Jerry McGuire*, in 1996. And perhaps most remarkable, Anna Paquin at the age of 11 won the 1993 Oscar for Best Supporting Actress for her role in *The Piano*.

1. A rough estimate of the number of movie actors and actresses in any given year that have the necessary credentials, have enough popularity, and are available to act in a film that might result in an Oscar win is 200. If all 200 available actors (assume equal numbers of male and female actors) have an equal probability of winning an award, what is the probability of any one of these actors winning an award in a given year?

_____

2. Pretend that you are an actor just beginning your career in big movies. You are one of the 200 "available" movie actors. Assume that your chances of being in a movie with a role good enough to get an acting award are 1 in 2. Assume that the probability that you will be nominated if you get a role is 1/5 and the probability you will win if nominated is 1/5.

(a) Use a random number table to simulate your career of 50 years. Design and conduct an experiment in which you select three different random numbers for each year. If all three meet your success criteria, you win an Academy Award for that year! List the years (if any) that you win an award.

_____

(b) In this activity, are the assumptions about probability good ones? Explain why or why not.

_____

_____

_____

22. What Is a Fair Price?

Context

Recreation

Math Topic

Expected value

Overview

This activity examines *expected value*, an average that arises when dealing with many repetitions of probabilistic situations in which different outcomes result in different returns. Expected value is very important in gaming situations because it reveals how much money will change hands in the long run, after many repetitions of the game. Furthermore, expected value can tell a player if the amount paid to play is a fair price.

Objectives

Students will be able to:

- demonstrate calculation of expected value.

- determine the long-term average return from a game.

Materials

- Calculator

- One copy of the Activity 22 handout for each student

- Two standard six-sided dice for each pair of students

Teaching Notes

What is a fair game? Try to get students to reason that a game of chance would be absolutely fair if no one gained or lost money over many plays. But no lottery or any other game of chance is absolutely fair. Games are always set up so that the *provider* (e.g., the state, the casino operator) makes money in the long run.

The exercises in this activity examine the following concept from probability theory:

$$\text{Expected value} = \sum_{i=1}^{n} f_i p_i$$

where f_i is equal to the prize for outcome i, p_i is equal to the probability of outcome i, and n is the total number of outcomes. Emphasize that this will yield a player's *average* winnings per play over a *large number* of repetitions. For state lotteries, this value usually is set to be about $0.50 per $1 bet. Thus, the regular lottery player can expect to lose half of his or her money in the long run. For lotto games where the large prize is quite rare, the experience of *most* players will be worse yet.

Answers

1. (a) The expected value is $2(1/4) + $1(1/2) = $1 average player winnings per play. So $1 is the break-even price over the long term, and a price of $2 will result in 50–50 split.

   (b) The expected value is $6(1/6) + $18(1/18) = $2 average player winnings per play. So $2 is the break-even price over the long term, and a price of $4 will result in 50-50 split.

(continued)

22. What Is a Fair Price? *(continued)*

(c) Students first will have to calculate the total number of possible outcomes. See if they can reason this out before helping them. The total number of possible outcomes is (12 • 11 • 10) / 3! = 220. Students are then given the number of ways that three, two, or one number can match out of the 220 possible outcomes. The expected value is $100(1/220) + $5(27/220) + $1(108/220) = $1.56 average player winnings per play. So $1.56 is the break-even price over the long term, and a price of $3.12 will result in a 50-50 split.

2. Students should assume that each roll costs the player $4, as calculated in 1(b). Then for 60 rolls, the player will spend $240. To determine the amount won by the player, multiply the number of times the player rolls 11 by $18 and the number of times the player rolls 7 by $6 and add these amounts. To determine the amount gained by charity, subtract the amount won by the player from the $240 spent by the player.

Extension Activity

Have students research the expected winnings per dollar wagered for various kinds of gambling—state lotteries, casinos, bingo, etc.

22. What Is a Fair Price?

A charity has set up some games to raise money. It is your job to calculate the break-even ticket price and the price that should be charged so that the charity will keep 50 percent of the money collected and pay out 50 percent in prizes. Assume that enough tickets to cover the prizes are always sold.

1. (a) The game is a coin toss where players toss a coin twice. Players win $2 if they get heads on both tosses, $1 for one head, and $0 for both tails.

   Break-even price   50–50 price

   _____   _____

   (b) The game is rolling two dice. Players win $6 if they roll a sum of 7 and $18 if they roll a sum of 11.

   Break-even price   50–50 price

   _____   _____

   (c) The game is a lotto game where players pick three numbers out of 12. The game operator picks the 3 winning numbers. If all 3 picks match (1 possible way), the player wins $100. If 2 of three match (27 possible ways), the player wins $5. If 1 of 3 match (108 possible ways), the player wins $1. (There is no prize for no matches.)

   Break-even price   50–50 price

   _____   _____

2. Run a simulation of part 1(b) above. Work with a partner. One of you should act as the player and roll the dice. The other should act as the charity and record the data. Pretend that the player pays the price calculated for a 50–50 split before each roll. How much has the player spent and won back and how much has the charity gained after 60 rolls of the dice?

   Spent by player   Won by player

   _____   _____

   Gained by charity

   _____

       Real-Life Math: Probability

23. Test for ESP

Context

Paranormal phenomena

Math Topic

Hypothesis testing

Overview

Belief in extrasensory perception (ESP) and other paranormal phenomena is rampant. Before we dismiss such beliefs, we should offer some methods for studying them. Any experiment designed to test for ESP will involve analyzing probabilities and gathering data.

Objectives

Students will be able to:

- conduct an experiment that tests for the presence of ESP.

- develop a statistical basis for accepting or rejecting the presence of ESP.

Materials

- One copy of the Activity 23 handout for each student

- One standard deck of 52 playing cards (no jokers) for each pair of students

Teaching Notes

Hypothesis testing is the crux of statistical analysis. Do data reveal a pattern that could be explained by a cause other than chance? The answer to this questions is not always clear. In this activity, students will be guided through an experiment testing for ESP. They will use what they know about probability and statistics to develop reasons for accepting or rejecting the hypothesis that ESP exists.

The experiment is very simple: the subject states the suit of a randomly drawn playing card without looking. The result, correct or incorrect, is recorded. The experiment is repeated 10 times.

The interesting part of this activity lies in deciding how many right out of 10 will constitute a positive test for ESP.

The acceptance level will be the number of correct answers above which the results will not be attributed to random guessing alone. However, students should recognize that every outcome, from 0–10 successes, has a finite probability of occurring by chance.

The model is binomial, with each independent event having a probability of ¼ (the chance of picking out one of four suits correctly entirely by chance). This model was discussed in Activity 11. The mathematical method for calculating these probabilities is

$$P_{n,\,m} = \binom{n}{m} p^m q^{(n-m)}$$

(continued)

23. Test for ESP *(continued)*

In this case, $p = \frac{1}{4}$, $q = \frac{3}{4}$, $n = 10$, and m runs from 0 to 10. The results of these calculations are displayed in the table below:

m	0	1	2	3	4	5	6	7	8	9	10
$P_{10, m}$	0.056	0.188	0.282	0.250	0.146	0.058	0.016	0.003	< 0.001	< 0.001	< 0.001

After students have all results from the trials, help them decide on the acceptance level. Make it clear that the acceptance level is up to the researcher. This is an issue in any kind of study. For an acceptance level of 7, the total probability that the subject will get 7 or more correct is only 0.003. An acceptance level of 6 means that there is a 1.9 percent chance that the subject will guess six or more correctly only by chance.

Answers

1. Results will vary. The table should be filled out completely.

2. The acceptance level is up to the student. But to make sure students are guided by the discussion above. For example, students should learn that selecting an acceptance level of 2 would yield over 50 percent incorrect acceptance that ESP is present.

Extension Activities

- Have students design other experiments of ESP on their own.

- Hand out a copy of experimental results from a scientific journal, and discuss how scientists use hypothesis testing to "prove" their hypotheses.

Name_____ Date _____

23. Test for ESP

Extrasensory perception (ESP) is an ability to detect, predict, or perceive events without the use of the usual senses (sight, hearing, touch) and without any prior knowledge. Other names for ESP include clairvoyance, telepathy and precognition. Some people claim to have this power. Persons claiming they have ESP are claiming to have a paranormal ability. How can you test for ESP?

1. Get together with a partner and set up the following experiment. Pretend that one of you claims to have ESP. The other will administer a simple test to see if the claim is true. The tester shuffles a deck of regular playing cards, then selects a card from the middle of the deck *without showing the card to the subject*. The subject, *without seeing the card*, declares its suit—clubs, diamonds, hearts, or spades. Record the result by placing an x under "Success" or "Failure" in the table below. Repeat the trial 10 times.

Subject name   Tester name

_____   _____

Trial	Suit Declared by Subject	Suit Actually Drawn	Success	Failure
1				
2				
3				
4				
5				
0				
7				
8				
9				
10				
Total number of successes in 10 trials				

2. (a) At what number of total successes out of 10 trials would you say your subject has ESP? _____

(b) Does your subject have ESP? _____

24. Busy Signals and Internet Service

Context

Computer services

Math Topic

Queues

Overview

So far all of the examples in this book have involved discrete (i.e., distinct) outcomes. For example the toss of coin has two distinct outcomes.

In this activity, the notion of a continuous distribution of outcomes is explored. Continuous random variables are particularly useful for problems in which events are happening over randomly varying intervals of time. Many such applied examples may be modeled by what is called a "Poisson process." The mathematical details of this process are beyond the scope of this book. Many textbooks are available on this topic.[1]

Many real-life problems have properties of a Poisson process. Cars passing a point on a road, clicks of a Geiger counter measuring radioactive decay, and the arrival of customers at a store are all examples. The latter example involves queuing theory.

This activity considers a queuing problem that is becoming all too common in daily life—dialing for an Internet connection and getting a busy signal instead. What's the probability that your fun surfing the net will be nixed because your Internet Service Provider (ISP) has no available connection?

Objectives

Students will be able to:

- simulate calls to an ISP and show the probability of receiving a busy signal under the given conditions.

Materials

- Calculator

- One copy of the Activity 24 handout for each student

- One random number table for each pair of students (see Appendix)

Teaching Notes

The mathematics involved in fully analyzing the queuing model for an ISP cannot be developed here. Instead, simplified cases will be considered that should be easier to understand. Part (a) should be self-explanatory. Part (b) calls for a simulation. Two-studnets should conduct the simulation as described below. Each trial represents 1 minute of time. Assume there are enough customers so that an average of 6 calls per hour are placed by customers desiring an Internet connection.

- A customer (Student 1) dials in an average of every 10 minutes, but the precise time of a call varies randomly. If 00, 11, 22, 33, 44, 55, 66, 77, 88, or 99 appears in a trial, a call is placed to the ISP. If any other pair appears, a customer does not call.

(continued)

[1] See, for example, Sheldon M. Ross, *Introduction to Probability Models*, 6th ed. (San Diego, CA: Academic Press, 1997).

24. Busy Signals and Internet Service *(continued)*

• The ISP (Student 2) can accept up to three simultaneous connections. If a customer calls and at least one line is available, there is no busy signal. When a connection occurs in a trial, Student 1 should report the next random number that is less than or equal to 60 to Student 2 as the amount of time the connection will be used. Student 2 must now consider that line busy for the reported number of trials (minutes). If all three lines are used, any incoming call will receive a busy signal.

• Student 2 must carefully keep track of which lines are in use, and for how many trials (minutes) they will stay in use. End the simulation after about 250 trials, simulating just over a 4-hour period.

Answers

1. (a) 6; (b) 64 out of 384, or 1 in 6, will receive a line, so the probability is 0.833 that the line will be busy.

2. (a) Below is a sample of how the record sheet might be used.

A=available; C=connection; –=in use; B=busy.

	1	2	3	4	5	6	7	8	9	10	11	12	13	14	15	16	17	18	19	20	21	22	23	24	25	
1st Line	A	A	C	–	–	–	–	–	–	–	–	–	–	–	–	–	–	–	–	–	–	–	–	–	–	
2nd Line	A	A	A	A	A	A	A	A	A	A	C	–	–	–	–	–	–	–	–	–	–	–	–	–	–	3, 0
3rd Line	A	A	A	A	A	A	A	A	A	A	A	A	A	A	A	A	A	A	A	A	A	C	–	–	–	
	26	27	28	29	30	31	32	33	34	35	36	37	38	39	40	41	42	43	44	45	46	47	48	49	50	
1st Line	–	–	–	–	–	–	–	A	A	C	–	–	–	–	–	–	–	–	–	–	–	–	–	–	–	
2nd Line	–	–	–	–	–	–	–	–	–	–	–	–	–	–	–	–	A	A	A	A	C	–	–	–		2, 4
3rd Line	–	B	–	B	–	–	–	–	–	–	–	–	–	–	B	–	–	–	–	–	–	–	–	B	–	

24. Busy Signals and Internet Service *(continued)*

Each block represents 1 minute. The last column gives the number of connections and busy signals. On the third trial, a number with repeated digits came up on the random number table, and the next number was 30. So the first line went into use for 30 minutes. On the 11th trial, the 2nd line went into use for 32 minutes, and on the 22nd trial, the third line went into use for 45 minutes (beyond the end of the sample table). After the 27th and 29th minutes, calls were placed that could not get in because all lines were in use. The 1st line again became available in the 33rd minute, but another connection was made in the 35th, leading to a busy signal in the 40th. A similar pattern occurs as the 2nd line becomes free in the 43rd minute and then a new connection is made in the 47th leading to a busy signal in the 49th.

(b) Results will vary considerably. During testing of the simulation, there was an average of 15 connections and 12 busy signals for runs of 250 trials. This represents a busy signal percentage of 12/27 or 44 percent. It is possible to calculate a theoretical value. This would be 9/26 or 35 percent for a system with three lines, six calls per hour, and an average service time of one half hour.[2]

Extension Activity

Invite a representative from a real ISP to talk about the many applications of mathematics needed for running such a business.

---

[2] See Ross, pp. 456–58. This situation may be studied as a queuing model called an *M/M/k* loss system.

24. Busy Signals and Internet Service

You use your modem to call for an Internet connection. The response: "beep, beep, beep. . . ." Rats! Foiled again! No net surfing tonight. How often does this happen?

1. Your Internet Service Provider (ISP) has 64 dialup lines (the same phone number can access any free line out of the 64). They have 384 customers.
   (a) How many customers are there for each dialup line?

   _____

   (b) If you and all other customers dial in at approximately the same time, what is the probability that *you* receive a busy signal?

   _____

2. The situations in part 1 are not very likely in real life. Rarely would all of the customers dial in at the same time. In this activity, you will use a random number table to model a simpler situation. The ISP will have 3 available lines. Customers will try to dial an average of 6 times per hour, at randomly distributed times. When they get in, they will stay connected for a random amount of time between 1 and 60 minutes.
   Divide into pairs. One student will represent the ISP and record the data; the other will represent customers trying to dial in.

   Customers (Student 1)   ISP (Student 2)

   _____   _____

   (a) Each trial will represent 1 minute. A trial begins with Student 1 checking the random number table. When both digits of the selected 2-digit random number are the same (e.g., 00, 11, 22), a call will be placed to the ISP. If there is a call, Student 2 will determine if a line is available and will record if a connection was made or if there was a busy signal on the following chart. Follow additional instructions given by your teacher.
   (b) After 250 trials, add up all calls placed and determine the percentage of attempts to connect that resulted in a busy signal.

   _____

   _____

3. What is a reasonable number of customers for the ISP if the call rate is 6 per hour?

   _____

4. In your opinion, what is an acceptable rate of busy signals for your Internet Service Provider? Explain your answer.

   _____

   _____

   _____

(continued)

24. **Busy Signals and Internet Service** (continued)
Record Sheet for Busy Signals and Internet Service

Write "A" for available, "C" for connection, a dash if the line is unavailable, and a circled "B" over the dash on the third line when a busy signal occurs. Each block represents 1 minute; each row is 25 minutes.

		Totals	
		C's	B's
1st Line			
2nd Line			
3rd Line			
1st Line			
2nd Line			
3rd Line			
1st Line			
2nd Line			
3rd Line			
1st Line			
2nd Line			
3rd Line			
1st Line			
2nd Line			
3rd Line			
1st Line			
2nd Line			
3rd Line			
1st Line			
2nd Line			
3rd Line			
1st Line			
2nd Line			
3rd Line			
1st Line			
2nd Line			
3rd Line			
1st Line			
2nd Line			
3rd Line			
TOTAL connections and busy signals			

25. Parking at the Mall

Context

Shopping

Math Topic

Optimization

Overview

In a mall parking lot, customers arrive and leave at random intervals. People like to park near the door, so those close-in spaces have the lowest probability of being available. Students will devise the best strategies so that they waste the least amount of time in the parking lot.

Objectives

Students will be able to:

- develop a parking strategy through simulations.

Materials

- One copy of the Activity 25 handout for each student

- One random number table for each student

Teaching Notes

Although there are theoretical constructs for handling these kinds of "optimal stopping problems," simulations will be easier for students to understand. Parts 1(a) and 1(b) suggest strategies that students should test. Optional part 1(c) suggests that students should make up their own strategies.

The "cost" in this problem is the total amount of time spent searching for a space and then walking to and from the space. To evaluate the strategies, students will use random numbers to model the availability of parking spaces and will then calculate a cost function to see how well the strategy worked. For this exercise, the cost function is 5 (number of sections searched) + 2 (number of sections away from entrance). The object will be to find a strategy that minimizes the cost.

Students will use a random number table to check if a section is available. They should consider that parking is available if the sequential random number picked is greater than or equal to the percentage representing the probability for that section. It will be helpful if students write down this list because the probabilities change from section to section.

Answers

1. The results will vary considerably. Here are some results from test trials:
   (a) average cost function = 40
   (b) average cost function = 36

2. Partners should compare results and report the best strategy.

Extension Activity

Go to a mall parking lot and make observations. Are the probabilities and cost function for this activity realistic? Refine these values and run new simulations.

25. Parking at the Mall

It happens every time you and your friends drive to the mall—you ignore the outer parking rows and snake through the first couple of rows nearest the door looking for a parking space. And there's always an argument.

"Why don't you take that one?" you say.

Your friend says, "No! We'll spend all of our time walking from the car and back."

You say, "No, we'll spend all of our time snaking around the inner rows looking for a space we'll never get."

Try doing some simulations to develop a compromise strategy. Use a random number table to simulate the availability of a space in a section of the lot. Work with a partner.

1. First, you find out that there are 25 parking sections at the mall. Section 1 is closest to the doors, Section 25 is farthest away. Furthermore, you find out that the probability of finding a parking place is 100 percent in Section 25, 96 percent in Section 24, 92 percent in Section 23. The probability of finding a parking place in a section decreases by 4 percent per section as the sections get closer in, so that the probabiltity is down to 4 percent by Section 1. Finally, you find that it takes 5 times longer to search a section by car than it does to walk a distance spanned by one section. So, in the trials below, the result will be a time cost equal to the time needed to search plus the time needed to walk to *and from* the mall entrance.

(a) One partner should try this strategy: Search Section 1 first. If no space is found (a random number less than 96 appears), go on to Section 2. If no space is found (a random number less than 92 appears), go on to Section 3. Repeat until a space is found, then record the time cost in the table below. Do at least five trials.

(b) The other partner should try an alternate strategy. For example, start with Section 12 (48 percent chance of finding a space). If no space is found, search Section 13. Repeat until a space is found, then record the time cost below. Do at least five trials. Use a separate sheet of paper to describe your strategy and present your results.

Strategy:	
Trial	Time Cost = 5 2 (Number of Sections Searched) + 2 2 (Number of Sections Away from Entrance)

 Real-Life Math: Probability

26. The Three-Door Problem

Context

Decision making

Math Topic

Optimization

Overview

This problem, with its counterintuitive answer, should be a lively culmination of these activities. A complete statement of the problem is given on the student sheet.

Although similar problems have been discussed in textbooks for years,[1] it was *Parade Magazine* columnist Marilyn vos Savant who made this problem famous in 1991. For a thorough discussion of the problem and a summary of the amazing array of wrong answers submitted to vos Savant, even from the mathematics community, see the magazine *Skeptical Inquirer.*[2]

Objectives

Students will be able to:

• apply careful analysis of conditional probability in order to make the best decision.

• perform a simulation to test a hypothesis.

Materials

• One copy of the Activity 26 handout for each student

Teaching Notes

Have students try to produce an answer for the problem before appealing to any theories of probability. The usual response is to say that it does not matter if you switch or not. Then, let students attempt to make their arguments based on probability theory, but do *not* correct them or give them any answers at this point.

Next, let them run the trials. The hint gives most of what they need to design the experiment. The students should be in pairs for the trials—one student is the host, the other the contestant. To use a random number table to generate a door for the prize, the host should move one digit at a time across the table. There are several possible ways to use the digits. Perhaps let 1–3 represent Door 1, let 4–6 represent Door 2, and let 7–9 represent Door 3, but skip any 0's.

(continued)

---

[1] See B.W. Lindgren, G.W. McElrath, and D.A. Berry, *Introduction to Probability and Statistics*, 4th Edition. (New York: Macmillan, 1978), pp. 59–60.

[2] Gary P. Posner, "Nation's Mathematicians Guilty of 'Innumeracy,'" *Skeptical Inquirer*, Summer 1991, pp. 342–45; and Kendrick Frazier, "'Three Door' Problem Provokes Letters, Controversy," *Skeptical Inquirer*, Winter 1992, pp. 192–99.

26. The Three-Door Problem *(continued)*

After the prize door is selected at random by the host, the host *must not* let the contestant know which door conceals the prize. The contestant then picks an initial door and tells the host. At this point, the trial is defined because there are two possibilities—either the contestant initially picked the correct door, in which case she would win by staying with her choice, or the contestant initially picked the wrong door, in which case she would win by switching. Check off the appropriate box—"Switch wins" or "Stay wins." For the fun of it, students may go through having the host "show" the contestant the other nonwinning door and offering the switch.

Answers

The contestant should always switch. The theoretical answer is that the contestant will win 2/3 of the time by switching. The easiest way to see this is to consider the final result as only two separate outcomes—the contestant's original door and *the set* of two doors including the one known to conceal a goat *and* the one the contestant can switch to. The probability is 1/3 that the contestant originally picked the correct door at random. The conditional probability that the prize is behind the door that the contestant can switch to is 2/3 because the contestant has already been shown by the host which of the two remaining doors *not* to pick.

There is an important point to remember about the trials—it is perfectly possible for 30 trials to yield values much different from the theoretical probability, even to the point where the "wrong" answer may look like the correct one. It would be a good idea to combine results from the whole class to get a better picture.

Extension Activity

Students may write a computer program to conduct thousands of trials of this model.

26. The Three-Door Problem

You are a contestant on a game show. The host lets you select one of three doors. Behind one of the doors a great prize is hidden: an expensive sports car. You win the car if you pick the right door. Behind the other two doors are junk prizes, "goats." First, you pick one of the doors at random. But before showing you if you have won, the host, who knows which door conceals the sports car, randomly opens one of the two doors you did not select, revealing a goat. The host then gives you a choice—stay with your original selection or switch to the other still-closed door.

1. To maximize your probability of winning the sports car, should you switch or not switch your choice of door?

   _____

2. Use what you know about probability to support your choice of door given the situation in question 1. What is the probability of winning if you switch doors? If you do *not* switch doors?

   _____

   _____

   _____

3. With a partner, design an experiment to test your answer to the three-door problem. Conduct trials using a random number table and report your results in the table on the next page.

(continued)

26. The Three-Door Problem (continued)

Trial	Prize Door	No. of Switch Wins	No. of Stay Wins	Trial	Prize Door	No. of Switch Wins	No. of Stay Wins	Trial	Prize Door	No. of Switch Wins	No. of Stay Wins
1				11				21			
2				12				22			
3				13				23			
4				14				24			
5				15				25			
6				16				26			
7				17				27			
8				18				28			
9				19				29			
10				20				30			

Hints: One of the partners is "host" and should use the random number table to decide which door the prize is behind. This partner *must not* tell the other partner, the "contestant," where the prize is located. The contestant then makes an initial choice of door. It is now possible to check off whether the contestant would have won by switching.

4. In what proportion of the trials did the contestant win by switching?

_____

Random Number Table 1

19	46	04	75	20	60	50	62	59	08	77	74	82	95	14	31	74	91	04	48	69	03	51	78	95
70	83	87	49	57	56	46	66	91	51	02	38	23	54	02	08	45	33	87	63	85	40	02	22	04
49	73	52	27	30	69	00	58	19	31	06	54	77	71	60	06	37	02	66	76	11	58	80	50	09
42	27	35	12	19	76	67	65	64	87	95	69	11	78	47	22	61	47	68	36	69	47	90	26	52
21	46	84	83	15	67	68	45	79	62	08	77	52	21	55	23	50	14	65	23	89	26	06	44	40
68	07	29	87	32	32	51	02	05	18	37	56	78	74	77	73	47	27	34	09	83	92	88	70	55
06	59	87	04	80	95	30	11	65	33	22	52	01	40	72	04	04	29	12	01	14	46	68	89	82
57	65	20	86	89	39	33	36	47	71	78	33	92	71	11	65	87	09	30	91	86	89	34	58	88
07	26	40	85	42	77	71	00	42	52	32	03	68	54	30	46	59	03	40	32	21	39	45	82	32
42	10	23	84	91	20	52	92	06	50	45	55	91	63	86	63	81	28	53	22	16	62	45	72	14
58	72	10	68	46	15	96	49	16	40	06	62	28	25	36	27	14	26	43	42	60	79	39	30	90
89	03	11	55	45	32	20	63	55	58	44	51	42	37	47	62	79	47	73	89	59	40	90	48	51
41	45	34	85	10	00	98	01	76	54	22	73	54	65	43	80	25	97	65	87	68	68	55	30	95
03	57	47	56	12	06	69	54	37	62	40	73	29	87	80	90	88	54	50	94	81	39	92	82	21
88	65	96	57	33	62	53	47	42	53	18	62	43	45	99	48	30	64	84	50	55	15	09	40	06
33	12	80	37	38	53	21	16	83	77	62	02	84	13	65	28	76	71	00	30	25	08	83	77	46
34	43	18	01	66	87	64	50	27	87	32	04	53	19	94	20	32	58	79	03	50	70	44	64	54
24	82	29	42	88	16	82	96	42	80	93	83	29	76	86	78	24	83	77	51	27	68	77	92	39
01	31	13	17	81	12	41	13	98	96	99	44	62	28	47	04	76	56	74	97	91	06	55	18	14
44	30	51	85	85	92	69	93	77	12	81	72	64	46	15	14	32	94	08	00	04	06	57	86	77
48	12	35	82	25	08	59	84	27	03	90	09	97	52	34	90	37	30	94	36	36	48	25	73	38
49	19	34	34	51	03	10	83	48	11	38	60	53	62	51	47	22	73	88	79	35	27	33	05	89
42	40	05	98	54	14	71	72	36	63	88	53	60	26	75	39	31	24	88	87	76	48	20	14	92
07	19	91	81	23	84	87	93	41	99	55	56	34	98	86	33	63	56	42	31	89	79	20	35	61
26	75	06	41	69	16	41	87	97	88	52	19	20	66	73	97	43	35	83	93	00	23	87	84	32
65	86	53	55	41	71	64	45	60	99	41	81	49	77	52	28	18	29	35	15	25	46	31	43	78
47	12	78	95	86	50	28	76	38	56	65	63	49	07	28	71	83	31	78	34	23	78	58	24	05
84	37	56	10	90	07	41	74	02	29	40	08	43	01	72	55	56	67	17	68	92	28	73	56	04
03	95	31	69	72	31	08	61	41	65	74	86	18	93	96	33	54	70	68	64	84	66	47	32	58
33	81	53	77	77	02	44	55	97	27	25	34	94	97	61	56	16	89	75	39	28	31	43	12	20
42	39	33	18	12	28	17	58	55	42	76	11	33	04	81	68	47	76	58	23	23	77	05	74	59
04	71	14	65	41	16	43	77	59	39	99	46	48	87	26	04	59	91	82	35	68	86	27	30	12
41	53	91	93	99	75	83	78	50	89	71	10	81	29	26	67	36	59	33	76	76	48	64	88	19
81	18	00	62	58	14	60	01	64	44	37	77	97	45	77	41	03	00	28	02	16	86	04	16	35
20	45	62	93	15	84	59	53	10	22	16	03	91	93	46	47	23	54	00	19	76	68	51	27	13
34	43	73	19	33	04	56	37	68	85	71	86	68	72	47	49	20	76	81	93	81	90	15	09	38
07	68	39	86	85	80	56	05	83	81	40	41	69	21	11	81	45	59	75	73	31	35	98	85	15
49	32	76	79	19	60	10	00	49	63	50	74	52	79	43	05	41	84	12	06	10	68	35	64	70
50	76	76	25	22	53	57	32	33	72	89	11	99	87	95	30	39	29	39	32	32	24	48	05	53
24	91	62	32	97	93	77	99	95	90	70	42	78	32	76	57	09	80	22	34	73	38	26	37	97

Random Number Table 2

01	57	14	23	15	12	44	52	49	05	79	26	47	97	53	18	44	62	93	14	03	88	07	02	76
22	43	29	78	82	06	75	99	00	30	66	37	30	26	72	61	75	45	03	55	43	60	34	44	89
57	77	14	21	07	55	85	27	38	25	12	96	43	97	41	20	29	54	21	14	20	49	96	69	08
49	93	96	60	04	01	69	55	64	08	73	48	07	76	96	88	93	80	77	86	93	89	97	00	92
22	50	63	74	20	23	16	61	93	36	86	22	82	25	30	78	98	41	33	75	58	81	26	30	93
70	47	12	54	40	19	40	86	85	06	27	57	88	67	94	88	10	46	81	26	43	27	95	00	68
41	16	22	47	35	08	38	06	23	85	72	50	19	54	44	97	86	99	27	48	30	89	09	80	46
87	26	61	00	87	05	02	96	08	58	33	07	05	93	74	30	14	34	87	23	51	32	15	58	12
42	54	66	19	41	19	95	10	24	44	62	96	04	21	49	65	48	43	04	29	52	79	60	76	91
61	57	05	76	36	67	39	01	96	56	97	22	99	34	40	95	56	84	75	49	33	25	88	09	50
70	49	28	91	20	71	17	17	62	30	63	38	02	18	55	71	37	82	65	91	01	50	84	25	50
61	28	20	51	26	63	77	05	32	88	50	60	86	33	06	20	41	05	85	38	86	57	33	66	93
43	28	89	53	80	15	19	92	00	69	94	66	69	06	60	78	13	62	78	14	67	06	19	77	65
01	96	55	09	30	73	33	67	52	22	82	68	80	54	64	09	31	55	20	81	85	37	16	08	66
20	87	93	58	82	21	54	79	77	60	54	68	36	91	51	95	13	80	92	33	42	42	85	74	20
97	93	14	76	30	95	57	36	04	60	78	27	52	26	10	82	51	71	59	62	38	84	55	73	69
61	70	91	37	40	84	07	47	88	58	78	12	22	17	04	79	44	29	01	60	50	63	37	49	85
09	84	26	10	92	25	60	28	41	67	33	53	61	47	25	51	56	21	35	66	67	74	29	97	81
65	35	61	80	68	94	24	72	72	55	49	79	90	35	77	50	12	52	05	61	28	09	31	84	71
22	61	59	47	26	25	55	53	16	47	04	25	60	80	42	95	61	02	12	38	54	36	32	92	98
84	38	17	53	86	15	14	78	92	27	95	78	59	09	86	84	87	66	80	95	27	14	12	12	00
57	88	38	06	47	92	29	83	76	00	64	83	04	45	93	80	20	86	06	92	36	30	45	62	89
79	07	74	33	42	77	95	87	41	43	83	14	26	02	24	91	49	27	19	75	89	41	63	75	29
41	55	96	84	17	62	49	31	12	96	71	89	98	37	64	30	93	03	21	97	56	57	46	54	35
83	93	19	78	88	87	77	92	74	17	12	65	17	41	36	28	22	04	01	29	76	15	50	54	02
77	49	82	43	92	72	49	87	96	31	65	45	09	83	86	18	33	63	71	65	39	21	46	74	49
77	21	89	56	99	31	99	08	78	54	63	91	93	01	74	24	72	34	44	26	93	90	37	09	68
03	70	32	76	63	82	02	92	58	08	28	81	12	72	28	82	52	81	04	84	01	04	80	46	31
29	32	53	18	51	58	51	92	90	95	12	60	45	19	59	70	22	07	02	12	04	08	89	91	12
59	43	59	15	02	29	82	11	46	12	37	61	11	68	84	53	28	33	91	13	71	09	44	29	64
22	71	62	12	61	16	60	74	01	58	99	00	41	08	01	98	39	07	24	75	71	94	38	96	29
22	95	39	27	71	35	44	27	06	15	57	82	22	12	64	16	59	70	82	37	15	49	63	36	31
58	28	82	59	89	48	21	42	46	03	79	19	90	07	80	94	37	79	38	57	13	87	69	23	83
90	23	69	96	61	77	29	13	58	57	93	25	66	22	82	33	47	36	65	63	88	16	31	08	31
58	32	56	75	53	16	56	15	48	21	24	04	96	77	53	97	26	61	97	41	95	83	50	87	24
36	37	42	21	58	44	11	07	40	48	54	77	97	86	61	79	67	28	89	17	08	02	03	68	79
00	39	20	45	09	70	77	56	25	85	92	38	59	63	42	43	16	07	89	86	59	48	06	81	95
51	45	57	17	07	99	39	45	23	24	47	30	18	39	45	13	61	06	46	67	13	48	61	48	96
75	36	28	26	55	78	54	23	72	73	56	42	90	24	27	19	13	10	26	47	62	79	23	57	85
10	77	44	39	35	20	59	16	23	05	00	51	18	63	33	71	52	76	64	85	12	58	03	84	58

Mock Lotto Tickets

01	04	23	43	44	48	03	25	29	35	37	44	08	13	14	23	25	28
01	05	13	31	33	34	04	05	07	08	34	39	08	13	24	39	40	41
01	05	29	30	48	49	04	05	17	26	35	44	08	19	20	37	43	45
01	06	14	29	30	32	04	05	19	27	29	37	08	24	29	32	33	39
01	07	17	37	38	48	04	09	23	25	33	37	09	14	18	21	23	33
01	08	23	28	35	40	04	11	12	15	42	46	09	14	31	41	43	49
01	10	13	15	26	48	04	13	17	19	36	37	09	19	22	28	38	48
01	11	15	19	28	36	04	14	18	21	31	45	09	24	30	33	39	44
01	12	20	21	23	44	04	14	31	34	41	47	09	26	27	33	45	49
01	15	25	35	41	43	04	18	30	42	46	48	09	28	30	35	40	48
01	24	28	40	46	49	05	06	07	15	40	42	10	14	21	23	48	49
01	31	32	33	39	40	05	06	09	17	31	35	10	15	26	35	44	48
02	03	24	39	43	47	05	06	11	21	42	47	10	16	21	29	30	33
02	03	36	37	38	47	05	07	12	19	25	38	10	18	20	21	31	33
02	04	09	17	20	34	05	07	20	39	40	44	10	20	22	25	34	45
02	05	09	26	39	42	05	08	11	20	41	40	10	20	31	11	18	49
02	05	21	25	26	42	05	09	15	43	45	46	11	12	21	39	45	49
02	07	11	19	46	47	05	10	15	22	29	30	11	18	31	33	35	46
02	08	13	16	26	48	05	11	15	28	32	48	11	33	38	42	43	46
02	09	10	27	36	42	05	14	29	38	39	42	13	14	41	42	43	47
02	11	29	37	39	47	05	18	31	40	41	49	13	15	26	32	36	43
02	16	30	31	45	46	05	21	27	32	40	48	13	24	38	42	44	46
02	17	18	26	41	45	05	26	30	38	40	47	14	18	23	24	37	47
02	17	24	27	30	42	06	07	16	25	28	42	14	20	21	26	28	33
02	19	29	40	43	46	06	08	11	16	23	48	14	28	38	43	47	48
02	19	32	37	17	49	06	08	26	30	44	47	15	17	20	29	39	42
02	21	22	32	35	45	06	09	12	18	23	35	15	18	33	37	45	46
03	04	05	09	26	39	06	10	11	23	28	49	15	26	34	43	46	47
03	04	06	15	22	47	06	11	12	22	32	41	16	17	24	36	37	45
03	04	12	25	28	47	06	12	13	15	21	29	16	19	20	25	26	37
03	04	17	22	40	48	06	12	15	25	30	37	17	21	25	26	31	43
03	04	22	37	41	45	06	16	20	22	23	36	18	23	24	31	44	45
03	05	06	22	24	32	06	20	22	26	42	46	20	21	22	31	35	46
03	05	13	25	27	39	07	08	09	21	34	38	20	21	30	31	32	46
03	06	08	10	15	32	07	12	16	19	31	36	20	22	27	35	40	48
03	06	10	11	38	42	07	13	24	30	31	46	20	29	36	39	46	47
03	07	26	37	40	48	07	13	29	35	36	38	21	29	30	41	42	45
03	10	12	23	28	40	07	23	28	32	45	48	21	30	32	34	35	43
03	18	18	25	38	47	08	09	17	30	37	40	22	27	31	35	41	49
03	18	19	27	29	43	08	10	25	38	39	40	25	27	31	33	35	40

Real-Life Math: Probability

Random Date Template

January	February	March	April
May	June	July	August
September	October	November	December

1	2	3	4	5	6	7
8	9	10	11	12	13	14
15	16	17	18	19	20	21
22	23	24	25	26	27	28
29	30	31				